KATHLEEN HOY FOLEY

FORGET ABOUT HEAVEN

Don't Yell At Me, Take It Up With My Dead Mother

AN INTER-CONSCIOUSNESS COMMUNICATION

Published in the United States by Women in Hiding Press.
www.womeninhidingpress.org

Cover Art by Kathleen Hoy Foley
Cover Design by Liz Geary
Copy edit by Dina Forbes
Composition by Liz Geary

Cataloging-in-Publication Data is on file with the Library of Congress.
Library of Congress Control Number: 2010940740
Foley, Kathleen Hoy
  Forget About Heaven / Don't Yell At Me, Take It Up With My Dead Mother
    p. cm.

ISBN-13: 978-0-9828558-4-3 (print)
ISBN-13: 978-0-9828558-5-0 (ebook)

PRINTED IN THE UNITED STATES OF AMERICA
10 9 8 7 6 5 4 3 2 1

FIRST EDITION

Dedicated to my mentors

Betty and Stewart

with immense gratitude for their life's work

It continues…

Nothing is given. All is earned.

Mary Patricia

Preface

Kathleen

This book about my mother is not the book I set out to write.

My mother was a pistol, beset with anger, filled to bursting with piss and vinegar. No one was spared her molten rage. Either you were the target or you were the witness. It was never a matter of *if* my mother would get to you, it was simply a matter of *when*. My intention for this project was to draw from a lifetime of "Mom" anecdotes, relaying them with a hefty dose of finely honed sarcasm. Because if I didn't poke fun at my mother's oftentimes extreme, maddening conduct, I'd end up poking myself in the eye with a fork before I even got started. Of course, given a choice, my mother would've chosen the fork and gladly done the honors. Despite her disapproval hovering around my cortex, at the end of this project, I would have a chronicle of a woman I so deeply loved, even though much of the time she behaved in ways that defied rationale and gracious manners.

Without a trove of courageous exploits to pull from, at least I could doll up my mother's outlandish deeds with a touch of Revlon Pink Lightning and a tad of biting humor, and in the process give a sort of voice to a woman who was flattened by silence but who every now and then allowed tenderness to peek out from the shadows clouding the sparkle in her blue eyes. She was one of a kind, my mom. If I couldn't write to provoke thought, at least I could write from the land of absurdity.

Plans organized, I embarked on a journey that I anticipated would be challenging and wacky with enough aggravation thrown in to make the wall next to me look like an extremely inviting place to bang my head. What I did not anticipate was how this path I'd chosen to tread would shift into the inexplicable and forever transform my perception of what I believed I knew and would reveal to me a woman—my mother—as someone I did not recognize.

1

One hundred pages of first-rate sass into the project, my mother died. This did not alter my focus or mission one iota. My mother and death were on a first-name basis. From my earliest recall, she'd been fixated on dying. Either she could die any second of any day, which I suppose explains why she balked at making long-range plans, since *I could be dead and buried by then;* or she was going to kill herself, one time threatening to stick her head in the oven and turn it on, only to later confess that the oven was electric and what good would that have done? And in her elderly years, complaining that old age wasn't for sissies and maintaining that all she wanted to do was die—apparently, the sooner the better.

Wish granted. During the silent dead of one winter night, tucked into her bed at the rehabilitation center, weakened by despair, my 84-year-old mother quietly and discreetly vanished from this life. Well in advance of her death, she had provided explicit instructions: she was to be cremated, her remains taken to Florida and buried next to her beloved husband, Jack. At her insistence, no fanfare, no viewing, no funeral. There was no use battling my mother, not even in death. You would not win; the wall next to your head would. *Wish granted.* Hence, on the day of my mother's cremation, my husband and I went out for a Chinese lunch and allowed the two people she had selected to tend to the details of her demise.

Exactly how long after her death my mother began trying to weigh in on my project, I don't remember. Only that it was several months. But I could be wrong about that. Maybe my mother had been *trying* for several months to get my attention simply to have me brush off any ethereal disruptions to my single-minded focus as the bothersome musings of a creative imagination, akin to a pesky mosquito buzzing my ear. Because by the time I actually folded and took notice of the repeated interruptions, my mother's voice was as loud, direct, and pushy as a radio commercial hammering my last nerve. And so distinctly "my mother" that she might as well have been standing right in front of me with her hands on her hips ready to throw a mango at me if I didn't stop and listen to her, which would come as no surprise if you knew our history with mangoes.

Okay! Okay! I mentally threw up my hands, scrolled back to page one, and with more reservations than I can convey, decided to play around and cater to this muse until either I got bored with wasting time or "my mother" ran out of words. Maybe a few minutes. Maybe an hour. Then I'd return to the task at hand. Slow and guarded, like picking my way across a minefield—that was the way to go. My mother had other ideas. Her voice was formidable and unmistakable, and soon enough I found myself leaning forward into this mysterious unknown and listening intently to the voice anchored there.

To say that I was cautious, skeptical, and unenthused by this turn of events is an absolute understatement. And not because recording the words of your dead mother as she is speaking them is dismissed as delusional in a culture possessed of little understanding or tolerance for what cannot be visually verified. I am unfazed by this bias. No, I was cautious, skeptical, and unenthused because it took very little to offend my mother during her lifetime, and owning to the energy I was intuiting, it didn't sound like much had changed. Whether she was here in the flesh or hovering about in spirit didn't matter—to give my mother any access to me emotionally or psychologically presented enormous personal risk for me. One word for involvement with my mother: boundaries. For many years, my husband and I were caught in a repetitive, vicious cycle of my mother's panicked emergencies and our failed interventions. I was not about to indulge in another pointless drill with my mother only to be berated with accusations after the heat of her crisis abated.

★ ★ ★

It was the 1980s, and my mother was halfheartedly filing for divorce from an abusive spouse—a man she'd hastily married shortly after the death of her first, much-loved husband. Halfheartedly, I suppose, because my husband and I had done a decent job of convincing her that she deserved a better life. Despite her reluctance, she agreed to begin proceedings and I offered to draft a letter to her attorney in her name. Wanting to give my mother every advantage possible, I tapped eloquent, professional terms to outline her position, describing what she had been subjected to during the union and what compensation she now deserved at its dissolution. It was compelling and well written. I was proud of that letter. My mother, on the other hand, was livid. "That don't sound nothin' like me," she yelled when she read it. Her anger about my failure to deliver left its mark, FOR-EV-errrr... I should not have been shocked when my mother fled back to the abuser before the ink had dried on the dotted line.

★ ★ ★

Suffice it to say I wanted nothing to do with once again facing accusations of putting words in my mother's mouth or accusations of any other dastardly offenses she could dream up to torture me with for the rest of eternity, since that's how long my mother can hold a grudge. But I love my mother. Plus, I was curious. And despite my reservations, there was significant reward in this for me—interaction with the mysterious and fascinating world of superconscious reality that I had just recently begun to study seriously. My heart's desire was to learn; my mother's heart's desire appeared to be to speak. So I defied my fear, held my breath, and said yes.

Sometimes my mother's voice flowed. Sometimes it came in fits and starts. Sometimes it stalled. Always there was a familiar cadence, a recognizable manner, and a defining attitude particular to my mother. Very quickly I realized that I would need a way to manage the incoming information without tainting it, or inadvertently flooding it with tangents of my own associations and unintentionally inserting my personal thoughts where they did not belong. To accomplish that objective, I decided to adhere to a strict, disciplined regimen—a serious departure from my typical writing routine of casual, unstructured musings and ponderings; continual preplanning and preparation; and obsessive use of Post-it notes to jot down thought-streams deluging me at inopportune moments. So, I would permit myself absolutely no anticipation, predictions, or expectations of how this project was going to unfold. And positively no guiding or controlling the outcome.

Basically, I showed up at the computer every weekday, synchronized my energy with my mother's, focused, listened, and transcribed. I offered suggestions for clarity and edited for cohesion. When writing chapters from my personal point of view, I adhered to the exact same regimen. Once I left the keyboard, I left the project. No reflecting on it away from my desk.

And so it began: *the abnormal became normal. The supernatural became natural.*

Right from the outset, my mother and I settled into a comfortable collaboration. Despite the practical challenges of inter-consciousness communication, the technical demands of the undertaking, and subject matter that was often disturbing and emotionally draining, the energy was consistently respectful, patient, and sincere. *Never* was the collaboration torturous, or even aggravating. As I sit here today composing this introduction, it occurs to me that not one time during this partnering with my mother did I even think about the wall next to me. If you knew my mother, no further validation of this work's authenticity is needed.

This is not to imply that this undertaking was ever easy. By its very nature, it could not be. It was exceedingly demanding, arduous, exhausting, and excruciatingly slow. But the most difficult part, my deepest challenge, my most profound self-doubt occurred when my mother began to transform and her normal cadence and her recognizable syntax, and her defining attitude began to make a dramatic shift. Her emerging voice, her newfound articulation was entirely foreign to me. This jarring change in her demeanor left me no cushion, no safeguard, nothing to fall back on for verification of accuracy or evidence of any error I might make in my interpretation or transcription.

I was a beginner with no foundation and hardly any experience in navigating this unknown terrain of a soul's evolution. And certainly no firsthand familiarity with a soul actually articulating and illustrating the process of its own evolution into its higher self. I counted on the comfortable security blanket of my mother's recognizable voice to guide this process to its conclusion. I could *do* my regular mother. I knew nothing of this new person—this strange, blossoming soul beginning to glow.

What if I was putting the dreaded words in my mother's mouth? What if I was making the story up as I went along? What was the truth? How could I possibly decipher it without my mother's "safe and familiar" traits to lead me?

For most of my years, my internal life had been controlled by dominating authorities with their bullying and finger-pointing, and their underhanded agendas, and the shrieking proclamations of doomsday cynics that scared the pants off me. Now they were back. But if I submitted to the echoes of those entrenched indoctrinations and misteachings and handed my power back over to the fear that had informed so much of my life, I may as well chalk this work off as hocus-pocus and return to my sardonic interpretation of my mother's life.

My other option was to accept the wonder of the process and allow its mysteries to unfold. Instead of imprisoning myself inside the darkened cell of fear, I could choose to venture forward into greater new horizons. I could agree to trust myself. I could agree to rely on my integrity and intuition for guidance. I could choose to trust in my mother's wings and embrace her evolution. I could always flee back to the dark if I couldn't bear the light. I chose the light.

So it is.

Patsy

I'm dead now. People don't believe that the dead cogitate. You think I thought so? You got another think comin'. When you're dead, you're dead. That's what I thought. That don't mean I didn't go to Mass. Wherever I lived, I went to church. I can still tell you all the names of them churches, too: St. Mary's, Our Lady of Sorrows, St. Raphael's, St. Gregory the Great, St. John's, Blessed Sacrament, St. Vincent De Paul. I never missed a Sunday or a holy day of obligation.

And I prayed, too. You don't know how much I prayed. I prayed to God for miracles. I prayed to Jesus. I made novenas to his Sacred Heart. I prayed to the Infant of Prague. Don't ask me who that is. *All I know is, Ask and you shall receive.* But I didn't receive nothin'.

I joined the "One Hail Mary a Day Club." The Blessed Mother was president. I said *more* than one Hail Mary a day. Nothin' happened. Maybe I ruined my chances by saying too many. I said rosaries. Once in the morning, once in the afternoon. Then before I went to bed. I read somewhere that if you pray the rosary three times a day for three days in a row and mention your request, you're guaranteed an intercession from Mary. I guess I didn't do that right, either, because Mary never listened to me.

I begged St. Jude. On my knees. He's the saint of hopeless cases, you know. He was supposed to *do* something. He didn't do nothin'. I waited. All I got was nothin'. I offered up thanksgiving. That's what the holy cards call it—*thanksgiving.* I had holy cards stuffed everywhere. In books. In my dresser drawers. In my wallet. I recited those prayers constantly.

It never worked. Nobody ever listened.

I was a miserable person in my old life. And nothin's changed. And I'm mad about it, too. You don't know how mad I am. I want to scream. I want somebody, anybody, to listen to me. *I want you to hear me!*

Nobody listened to me when I was living. Nobody. Except Jack.

That was my husband. I didn't trust nobody except Jack. But he died in his forties. Diabetes. Congestive heart failure. His feet were going. He had to sleep sitting up. When I lost him, I lost everything. I didn't have nothin' after that. Jack was a perfect husband. He loved me. I loved him with all my heart. That's not easy for somebody like me to say—I don't go in for all that love stuff. But, Jack…oh, I don't want to cry, damn you. Now see what you did? You made me cry. I hate crying worse than anything. Nobody ever minded me when I cried except Jack.

Nobody cares about this, but when Jack died, I died. At his wake, when I saw him laid out in his brown suit, every hair in place like always, looking like he was just asleep, I started to drown. He *couldn't* be dead. He *couldn't* be. I was suffocating. I couldn't breathe. I couldn't breathe. I started screaming and screaming. And couldn't stop. I kept screaming and screaming, "I want to die! Let me die!" I threw myself in his coffin. I remember screaming and clawing at his body. I *had* to go with him. *Nobody would listen to me.* I *had* to die! How could Jack leave me alone like that? He promised he'd stay with me. *He promised.*

★ ★ ★

On the way to the hospital, Jack swore to me that he wouldn't die. I was holding him in my arms. He was so out of breath he could hardly talk, but he said, "I'm going to make it, honey." My son, Tom, was speeding, blaring the horn. Cars stopped to let us pass. And Jack waved *thanks* to them. He was having a massive heart attack and he was still *polite.* I never got over that. Jack was the nicest man I ever knew. Everybody loved Jack. When we got him to the emergency room, the doctors promised me he'd be okay after they got him hooked up and took him to intensive care. I believed them. When they wheeled him down the hall, Jack, as weak as he was, lifted his hand and waved goodbye to me. The doctors told me—*they told me*—that as soon as they got him upstairs, he'd be okay. *I believed them.*

I was pacing in the waiting room, sobbing and praying, when a nurse marched up to me.

"Your husband's dead." That's all she said: *Your husband's dead.* I let out a bloodcurdling scream. And then that nurse smacked me across the face so hard she rattled my teeth. I stopped screaming. I stopped crying. All I could feel was that nurse's hand stinging my cheek. And I drowned.

★ ★ ★

My sons and son-in-law tried to pull me out of the coffin. I fought and kicked. I screamed bloody murder. Why wouldn't they just let me go? I hated those damn kids for pulling me away from Jack. And I hated Jack for dying. I kept screaming and screaming. Then somebody shoved some pills in my hand and made me swallow them with water that smelled like sulfur. After that, I just sat and stared. I didn't say nothin' to nobody. Not even when they talked to me. I just sat and stared. And hated every one of them.

I always kept how much I loved Jack to myself. I wanted to tell him, but I couldn't. I couldn't get the words out. Every time I wanted to tell him how much I loved him, the words would stick in my throat. I hate myself for that. I could hear what I wanted to say to him in my head—nice words, like poems—but I couldn't push them out. And I'd get so mad at myself. Then I'd be real mean to him. I always felt sorry after. But I never could tell him that, either. I was miserable to him a lot. But Jack was never mean to me. Not one time. I don't know why he put up with me. I didn't deserve his love. I was a horrible woman.

2

Kathleen

I remember the viewing in that dusty, rundown funeral parlor that hovered on the cusp of ratty. Except for the sickly, throat-biting sweetness of lilies and roses wired into vivid, extravagant memorial sprays and the bright orange and blue splashes of tropical birds of paradise stuck into gray cardboard vases, everything else felt low rent. The pimply faced undertaker must have scored all his stuff at a going-out-of-business sale on the seedy side of town, because the furniture felt like it should've been held together with duct tape and thumbtacks, though I didn't notice any. But cheap was everywhere.

I wanted my mother to rise above cheap that day in that sad, stale mortuary. I wanted her to radiate grace and poise in that shoddy, sickeningly sweet room with the acne-scarred kid-mortician in the ill-fitting black suit playing host. I wanted her to claim refinement in the midst of her anguish and package her grief in a few poignant tears tended to by a lace hanky. I wanted her to float above the death and misery swallowing her and honor herself—at least for those public moments—with self-respect. I wanted to look up to my mom at this time of her most profound, intense grief and be buoyed and astonished by her remarkable dignity. I wanted her to be Jackie Kennedy.

She wasn't. My mother made a spectacle of her grief, shrieking and howling like a rabid animal. At the first sight of her husband in the casket, she screamed—piercing, wet, sloppy screams. Screams of naked agony. Her sheer jolts of stark panic electrocuted the reverence, startling the assembled bereaved, shattering all notions of quiet prayer and destroying the calming efforts of Muzak purring from hidden speakers. I watched, mortified, as she grasped and clawed at the corpse; as her entire body convulsed in an epileptic fit of anguish and she threw herself into the coffin, clutching the cadaver, screaming. And screaming. Battling with that corpse, begging it to live. Begging for her own death.

"STOP IT, MOM! STOP IT!" I wanted to shout. I couldn't bear the shame of her crazed, wild-eyed public frenzy, the spittle frothing at the corners of her lips. I couldn't endure her agony, her uncontrolled keening. I didn't want to witness her stripping herself, or watch her thrashing against the walls of panic she was trapped in while she ruptured into thousands of bloody pieces. Wrestling the swells of my own submerged fears beginning to quake, I rushed to sit and averted my eyes, staring down at my wedding rings and trying to blot out my mother's screams. Trying to block the low grunts and the heavy thumping and scuffling of my husband and brothers disentangling her from the casket. Trying to ignore the muffled groans and the stunned silence of the onlookers. Trying not to feel the scorch of humiliation as if it were a fire licking my cheeks.

In the midst of this garish pandemonium of intimate grief, high-pitched squeals, the cries of "Not Jack! Not Jack!" erupted from the back of the room. Startled, I glanced over my shoulder just in time to see my aunt collapsing to the floor in a great flourish of dramatic fainting as my uncle struggled in a useless effort to keep her deadweight girth upright.

After my mother finally crash-landed back to earth thanks to the pills and glass of water somebody had shoved into her hands—and a few minutes before she turned into a zombie—she snarled and glared at my aunt as if her sister-in-law had flown in on a broom specifically to steal the spotlight and snatch all the pity. Which was hardly a stretch, since in real life, Aunt Dot was a hypochondriac and never missed an opportunity to hijack a captive audience for the specific purpose of garnering sympathy for her endless imaginary ailments. And there she was, grabbing the glory at my father's wake by upstaging my mother's vulgar hysteria with the consummate, sympathy-evoking, swooning-damsel routine. My mother may have been insane with grief, but she zeroed in on that calculated sham with dripping fangs and seething daggers that she sank into Aunt Dot by way of my neck.

You did not want to cross my mother. Unfortunately, your mere existence already aggravated her, so angering my mother did not require much. It is a colossal understatement to say that my mother detested *any* attempt to gain sympathy, especially from her—my mother *received* sympathy, she *did not* grant it. So, as quick as a rattler strike, my mother retaliated against Aunt Dot with contemptuous, guttural digs meant specifically to be overheard all the way to the back of the room: *What the hell is she doing here? Who the hell does she think she is? Look at her acting like she's passing out. Horse's ass. She's nothing but a damn hypochondriac. She has some nerve. I can't stand her.* I sat stiffly beside my mother, cringing. Wincing at her cruelty. Absorbing her icy rage. Hoping to God that my body would soak up the volume of her rampant spite fixed on the kill. I needed her to be *nice.* She wasn't.

Yes, I remember that viewing. It was a tattered, bloodletting circus. It was pain ripping and scraping at the walls. A dive into the depths of raw, unleashed agony. It was the screams of a butchered soul. It was the spectacle of my mother disrobing herself in the presence of a gawking audience. It was a disgraceful display of her distain—her living, breathing hatred—directed outward, aimed at the bull's-eye of friendly, beating hearts.

I never understood. And I never forgave her.

3

Patsy

Kathleen exaggerates. I don't know what she's talking about. But if she doesn't watch it, she's gonna be on my list. And once you're on my list, you don't get off it.

I always said, *I don't get mad, I get even.*

Patsy

I keep forgetting that I'm dead now. Maybe that's why I'm having such a hard time staying mad; I dunno. Before, all that crap about her father's viewing would've made me so spittin' mad at Kathleen my head would've been spinning and that would've been the end of her. I'd never say another nice thing to my daughter. I still think that way, but being mad just don't *feel* the same no more.

I've always been the ornery type, you know. If you made me mad, I'd just stop talking to you. There was nothing you could do. I don't accept apologies. And I never made them, either. Anyhow, I was never one for talking. I hate women who talk too much.

Nobody ever accused *me* of talking too much. I never had much to say. Besides, talking was for smart people, and I was dumb. I would never admit it, but I liked words—a lot. *Don't you dare tell on me.* I'll call you a liar if you do. I never admit to nothin'.

I used to read a lot. It was a good way to pass the time. I didn't read none of those stupid brainy books—I wasn't one of those conceited women with tight skin who put on airs. I hate those stuck-up women. I never talked about the books I read, except to say they were boring, but I read every single day and went to the library every week. The librarian even knew me by name. I felt kind of good about that. I wish there were some books around here. Or at least a television to stare at. There's nothing to do but think. And thinking always got me into trouble. But I don't have nothin' else to do to kill time.

I don't understand none of this. If I'm supposed to be dead, how come I keep remembering stuff? How can I be dead as a doornail and still see pictures in my head? Why do I keep seeing my sister Bobby? That's really aggravating. I hated my sister. And why do I keep thinking about words? Words! Words! Words! I'm sick of it. This must be Hell. All this thinking about Bobby. And words all over the place that don't make no sense. I can't figure out what none of this means. I'm gettin' really pissed off.

I'll tell you one thing, my older sister liked girl sex. That's all I'm gonna say.

Kathleen

My mother didn't talk. I don't mean that literally. She had a list of cuss words that she'd let rip when she had a mind to. And she'd announce what we were having for supper if you asked. Plus, she complained constantly. Fatigue was high on her list. *First time I sat down today,* she'd groan every day at 5:30 p.m., just before lowering herself into the chair opposite my father after she'd fixed the last of seven plates with meat, mashed potatoes, and canned peas and filling five jelly jar glasses with milk and two Pyrex mugs with percolated coffee.

But she didn't *talk* like my friends' mothers, who leaned across kitchen tables to make a point or spread gossip. Or rag about odd family members. My mother didn't chat about books or childrearing. She never discussed intellectual concepts. She didn't offer opinions or initiate conversation. Or ask anybody for anything. When she had to, my mother responded to direct inquiries or group exchanges with brief, awkward remarks. Mostly, she sat quietly.

It's not that she was a refined woman. She had jazz and sass. And once in a while, she'd burst through that invisible restraint that was making her mute and ignite my world with sparkle and brilliance. And I'd see her soul on fire. As if she were tap dancing on the flames she herself lit. Like how she told me she did when she was a little girl—Shirley Temple style, bow anchored in her banana curls—shuffle-hop-stepping across the school stage to the beats of the boogie-woogie and the clamor of loud applause. One time when the house was empty except for us, she even talked to me about poetry. She actually *understood* the complicated verse and rhymes that knotted my brain.

Every once in a while, though, a mysterious something inside her gave way, an outburst of anger unrelated to an outwardly bland circumstance. Those times she'd burn fierce and swift—an instantaneous eruption of molten fury. It meant big trouble for you if at that particular moment you were on her wrong side, because you'd end up a pile of cinder before you even knew what the hell happened. She wouldn't tell you why, either. She'd just cast her weighted pall over the entire household and withdraw into the silent treatment that lasted as long as she damn well pleased. Which could mean the entire rest of your life if what she imagined you did pissed her off enough. It was always up to her target to figure out what made her so mad. If it wasn't me on the receiving end of her wrath, I'd just wait it out, trying to humor her with compliments and Tastycakes. Eventually she'd unfreeze—no explanation given—and I'd return to tottering across eggshells until the next time. No, my mother would give no explanation.

It's made me frantic over the years, my mother's refusal to talk. As a kid, sometimes I'd think she was dead, propped up there in the corner of the couch on top of the cushion with the upholstery worn down to the cotton batting, blank-staring at Red Skelton cavorting across small-screen television. But then she'd raise that Raleigh to her lips, inhale like she was sucking oxygen, hold her breath, and exhale a quiet lake of white smoke that smelled like perfume to me. That's when I'd breathe. And smile. She wouldn't say a word though. She'd just go back to staring at the television.

I longed for my mother to *talk*. But she just didn't.

6

Patsy

Kathleen has a short memory. She accuses me of not talking? Aren't I talking now? What about what I already *told* her? I *told* her a long time ago that I hated my sister. I already told her that I had to share a bed with her. I *told* her that my sister did things to me. What else does she want from me? She should learn to listen better. I *hate* to repeat myself. What do I have to do, spell everything out for her? Nothin' I did ever satisfied my daughter. No reason to think it's gonna change now. Anyhow, I don't have a way with words like she does. And if I start talking, I know my daughter will just accuse me of being stupid.

But if she wants me to paint a picture—then damn it, I'll paint her a picture. See how she likes what I have to say. When I get done, she'll be sorry she asked. I'm only doing it because I'm dead and bored and I don't have nothin' else to do.

7

Kathleen

I had to sleep in Bobby's bed, and she did things to me. That was the bomb that my mother would calmly drop, usually while we were strolling through an antique shop or standing in the checkout line at Kmart while she fiddled around in her wallet for five dollars to pay for a blue-light special. From the tone of her voice, she could've been musing over café curtains. The worst, though, was the long-drawn-out rides to the casinos down in Atlantic City. There's nothing much to occupy a mind when you're driving through miles and miles of the Pine Barrens to reach the Jersey Shore. No means of distraction and definitely no immediate means of escape. Blacktop and scrawny pitch pines and a smattering of rusted mobile homes. That's it. Blacktop and pitch pines. And my mother. And her Raleighs. *I had to sleep in Bobby's bed,* and she did things to me, she'd say, exhaling that bomb along with a stream of chalky smoke from her cigarette. Then total silence. Now, what was I supposed to do with that? What did she want from me?

It's not like she ranted and raved and spit wooden nickels when she dropped the Bobby Bomb. It's not like she asked me what I thought. It's not like she clarified anything, like telling me the story of what the hell happened. It's not like she cried. She'd just drop the Bobby Bomb and fall stone silent. "Mom," I'd say, "that's horrible." To which she'd just pick up a dusty figurine and say, "Isn't this cute?" Or push wadded dollars into the salesclerk's hand and stare at her items being stuffed into a paper bag. Or simply shrug her shoulders and take another long drag on her Raleigh while she gazed at the landscape speeding past her window.

That was it. That was all it ever was. The Bobby Bomb. Cold silence. And her eerie slide into fairy space.

Patsy

I *hate* doing this. I don't even know why I'm bothering. I hate talking more than anything else in this world. I'd rather clean shitty toilets than talk. You don't know how much I hate talking. Before I say anything, I want you to know I don't have no good words. I don't know how to say things. I'm not smart like Kathleen.

Anyway, there's nothin' to say. I lived in a little house in Fieldsboro, New Jersey. Everybody called it The Homestead because Daddy built it himself and it was out in the country, I guess. There were five of us kids then—three boys and two girls. Then Nanny and Jesse, Daddy's parents, came to live. Mother loved babies and always took them in, so there was always foster kids coming and going. Sometimes the dining room was so full of crying kids and cribs and playpens that there wasn't no room to walk. I couldn't take those kids, but I had to help care for them anyway. Then Mother and Daddy adopted one. I don't know what they saw in that kid, but everybody treated him like little Lord Fauntleroy. They all tried to tell me that he was my new brother—I was a teenager by then. That kid was never my brother. I could never stand that kid. I still can't. Being dead don't change it.

All I know is that the house wasn't big enough for everybody even before Nanny and Jesse came to stay. I don't know why they had to live with us, only that they didn't get along too good—Nanny was a real pistol, and Jesse was deaf and blind. I remember I was around twelve years old when I had to give up my bedroom for them. I loved my little room. It was real quiet in there. It was downstairs in back of the kitchen and nobody bothered me. And Mother was always close by. One day she cut out hundreds of tinfoil stars and pasted them on the ceiling right over my bed so I wouldn't be afraid at night. Every night I stared at them stars before I fell asleep.

I threw a real temper tantrum when Mother told me I had to move upstairs into Bobby's room, but it didn't do no good. I hated Bobby. Nobody ever saw how mean she was to me. I didn't have no trouble with my brothers. But Bobby was a sneak. She'd hurt me whenever she caught me alone or when nobody was looking. She'd grab my hair and pull real hard until I cried. She'd call me names like *greasy spic*. I didn't want to have to be alone in that room with her, but I didn't have no choice. I'll never forget, there was only one bed, a twin — rusty iron with white paint chipping off. I'd wedge myself between the wall and mattress and try to make myself invisible. I'd shrink myself into a tight ball so I wouldn't accidentally touch her because I hated her so much.

But then… Then there were other things… And I'd hold my breath for as long as I could and beg Jesus to make her forget that I was there. But Jesus didn't bother to help me.

The springs in the mattress squeaked every time Bobby rolled toward me. I can still hear it — that squeaking and creaking. I couldn't stand that sound. *I still can't.* I remember shaking and shaking knowing what was coming next.

That squeaking in the mattress. Her cold hands on me. I can't talk no more! I can't breathe. I know I'm dead — but I'm suffocating! Help me! I can't breathe!

9

Patsy

Nobody knows what it was like. Nobody knows what it was like to have to sleep with a queer. You don't know what it's like not to have names ugly enough to call her. You don't know what it's like not to have the words to tell things right. You don't know what it's like when nobody will listen to you.

10

Patsy

That twat was nine years older than me. She was always the favorite. Bobby couldn't do no wrong. In our house, she was the queen bee. Yeah, right. She wasn't no queen, she was a queer and a horse's ass. Just looking at her you could tell how ugly she was. Her nose grew out of her face like a beak. She reminded me of a hawk. Naked, she turned my stomach. Her boobs were long. They looked like two empty bags of droopy chicken skin. And her flabby gut reminded me of the dead jellyfish I used to poke with driftwood down at the Atlantic City seashore. I remember her arms. They were hairy like an ape's. And she never shaved her armpits. Or used deodorant. She held me down with those hairy ape arms. She smelled like horse shit.

I didn't know what sex was, boy or girl. All I know is that what she did to me hurt. It burned. Did you ever scald the tip of your tongue? That's what it was like. Like a lit match held to your tongue. But *down there*. I remember the stink of something I don't have no name for—a mix of menstrual blood, drool, and sweat? Spunk. That's what it was. The room stank of spunk. I can still smell it. I remember how it choked me. I couldn't breathe.

Her fat fingers hurt me. Ripping and shoving. Her fingers poked and rammed into where I pee. How would you like that? How would you like to feel yourself tearing? In my head I kept hearing a zipper. I could feel prickly little bubbles of blood crawling out of me *down there*. I wanted to wipe it away—I was *crazy* to wipe myself. I remember my bones *down there*. I *felt* them turning black and blue. I could *see* my bones *down there* turning black and blue.

I was so ashamed, because I stank. I could *smell* myself. I could *smell* my breath. It smelled like sour milk. I could *smell* my blood. I smelled like a dirty animal. I smelled like the chickens that mother slaughtered in the kitchen sink. I was petrified to move, but I kept shaking. And shaking. I'd spit up. But it didn't go nowhere. It just stayed in my throat. I can still taste it.

The nights Bobby brought her lezzie girlfriend over were the worst. She'd pull me into the middle between the two of them like I was a rag doll. They laughed. And did filthy things to me. With their hands. Their mouths. With…with …other things. Dirty things. Things I don't want to see.

Every time after she was done doing what she did to me, she'd groan like a bull and then she'd beat me to a pulp. Blow after blow. Fist after fist after fist. In my stomach. On my back. Pounding. Pounding. I felt my spine vibrating. *You better keep your mouth shut, Patsy. Or, I'll kill you.* She'd say that over and over. A hundred times. Huffing and wheezing those same words. *You* (hit)…*better* (hit)…*keep* (hit)…*your* (hit)…*mouth* (hit)…*shut* (hit)…*Patsy* (hit)…*or* (hit)…*I'll* (hit)…*kill* (hit)…*you* (hit).

You better keep your mouth shut, Patsy, or I'll kill you. I'll never forget them words.

11

Kathleen

Part of me wanted to know what happened to my mother. But mostly I didn't, so petrified was I of what she would blurt out. So terrified that she'd corner me in her darkness and drench me with her intense, miserable emotions and trap me in the black abyss of her misery and not let me go. If allowed, she'd swallow me whole and never spit me out.

My mother did not *reveal* her past, she *dumped* the filth of her pain on me. Crashed a garbage truck straight through civil boundaries, pounded the red button, and discharged a shitload of sewage. My mother didn't narrate a story. She inflicted punishment with it. From her prison of ugliness where she dwelled, my mother exacted verbal revenge against the heavens and any innocent bystander within earshot. She'd cut and shock with vulgarities, goading me into sympathetic responses that she would then just shrug off.

I didn't want my mother to tell me what happened to her—she'd rip my heart out of my chest and leave it to pound until it bled out its last beat. Let it hang there while she pecked away at it with her gloom until it was withered and mummified into a wasted, brittle, unusable carcass. I didn't want to be tormented with her naked, butchered body. I didn't want her exposing it to me, brandishing it about like a spiteful flag in the face of the enemy when I was the only one present and I wasn't her enemy. I was desperate not to be imprisoned with her and her ripped, bloodied, little-girl vagina with no means of escape, no oxygen to breathe. I was frantic to protect myself from being impounded by the weight and malice of my mother's enormous, uncontrolled pain. I was terrified, *terrified* of being pulled into that hell where she lived. Where I would die.

12

Kathleen

We'd have visits. A week. Two weeks. Three weeks long. She lived in Florida. I was in New Jersey. I'd think I could pull it off. I'd dream of beaches and strolling in the sun. Going to the casinos. Laughing. Lunches out. Antiquing. I was crazed for those visits to work. I'd plan. Fantasize. Develop strategies. I'd obsess about empathizing with my mother, imagining a host of intolerable scenarios that I'd effortlessly resolve with tender compassion. I'd be the loving, understanding daughter. No matter what! And I failed every time. Never mind that I began each visit with a heart brimming with charity; I descended always into martyrdom with its flustered, jagged edges, sinking finally in the quicksand of churning resentment. It never took long. Sometimes a couple of days would pass before I'd start to think that one of us had to die. Other times my pipedream just oozed into the dirt and all my good intentions disintegrated before the visit even began. Once, after we'd been on the road for two days and were within a mile of my mother's house, my husband, Phil, said, *No matter how slow I drive, we're still going to get there.*

13

Kathleen

My mother was just a little thing, pretty and well-groomed until her last cogent days. But her physical presence disguised a muscled, emotional stamina—a skilled talent for strong-arming with silence that she wielded like a sledgehammer. All that compacted fury and chaos of her hurt quaked and vibrated immediately below her words like a volcano threatening the earth from its submerged depths. Silent tantrums—she used them to obligate me, to force her will on me. Locked inside emotional terror, I was panicked that my mother would destroy every last sensibility I possessed with those silent tantrums. I didn't know how to stop her. *I didn't know how to stop her.* I *couldn't* stop her.

14

Kathleen

Early on, my mother implanted the threat of her imminent death in my child mind, and I'd lugged that foreboding around like a weighted corpse ever since. Tiptoeing around her. Trying not to upset her. Trying to love her. Trying. Trying. *Trying.* Failing. Failing. *Failing.* She stoked my dread with below-the-belt accusations and gruesome pronouncements: *You're trying to kill me. I know you—when I get old, you'll lock me in your cellar. I'm going to end up a bag lady on the streets, wait and see. When I die, just throw me away in the garbage.*

My mother carried the Grim Reaper around in her back pocket. And who would she blame when *he* broke free?

15

Kathleen

So, I recoiled from my mother's presence. Hid from her. Dodged her company whenever possible. When I couldn't escape physically, I fell to words—lots of them. Nonsense. Mindless gossip. Compliments. Flattery. If that didn't work, I'd invent chores, missions. Let's *(fill in the blank)*: build a patio; bake a cake; go to Publix, Kmart, Walgreens (for the hundredth time). Anything I could pull out of my brain to distract her from hammering at my heart.

We were locked in a battle, my mother and I. She wanted my life. And I was throwing up the crucifixes to stop her. She was trying to haul me back to the 1960s, to the front steps of our Cape Cod on Mark Twain Drive where we'd sit after dinner on warm evenings and gossip about the neighbors. Where she gloried in her castration fantasies and set her sights on Mr. High and Mighty.

Not that Mr. High and Mighty didn't deserve my mother's loathing. Wearing Bermuda shorts hiked clear up to his man boobs and support hose stretched up to his knees, Mr. High and Mighty strolled the sidewalks of our suburban development with his nose stuck up in the air like he was God's gift to women. In my mother's opinion, that alone qualified him for castration. Unfortunately he made the mistake of asking her to donate to the Holy Name Society, of which, he bragged, he was a *very important member*. That stunt doomed him. But Mr. High and Mighty's biggest, most unforgivable sin—the one that sealed his fate in my mother's mind—was in his pants which he obviously couldn't keep zipped. What? Eight, nine, a dozen kids he'd already forced on his poor wife, a pale, worn-down woman who never left the house? Now she was pregnant *again*? And rumor was that most were delivered by Caesarean section. Poor soul. My mother would have happily taken a scalpel in her own hands and slashed Mr. High and Mighty's private parts to bits. And I would have joined her.

My life revolved around my mother there on Mark Twain Drive. Our camaraderie was silken nectar. The sense of affection and sisterhood, ambrosia. I reveled in the balm of our shared humor. Only it wasn't real. More than anything, it was a form of play. A distraction. It was make believe fun driven by cryptic desperation. I wasn't her friend. I was her emotional lackey obsessed with putting the joy in her veins.

Back then, I was somebody she didn't fear. Somebody who didn't make her feel inferior. Somebody incapable of intimidating her. That I was shattered and broken never crossed her mind. She did not notice that I had no face. No body integrity. No spirit. She did not see that I had been scrubbed away by the torment I'd been subjected to for years and only recently rescued from, and that now I was in the grip of new terrors. Torments I didn't know how to stop. Panics I couldn't control. So I anchored my splintered self to her, holding myself together by fastidiously devoting attention to her needs, all the while hoping in some way I could repay the enormous debt I owed her.

16

Kathleen

My mother had permitted me to live — she had not disowned me for my *disgrace*, for how I'd let her down, *for what I had done*. My mother did not forgive. One black mark was all it took and you were done. Finished. Gone. *Don't bother comin' back.* It'd just be a waste of your time.

But not only did my mother allow me to be in her presence, she shared cigarettes and laughter with me. Since my crawl back from the dead — which she regarded as me learning my lesson — her temperament had turned warm and friendly, and my frozen bones melted gratefully into this unusual personal hospitality. Really, though, her new openness had nothing to do with helping me recover — she never recognized or admitted that there was ever anything I needed to recover from.

In a house fueled with burgeoning testosterone, I think she needed a friend. And there I was — a compliant, housebroken puppy eagerly hanging on to her every word, thanking God every minute that she hadn't conked me over the head with a brick and tossed me down the sewer.

17

Kathleen

A lifetime had passed since the 1960s and those days of my concentrated, devoted attention toward her, yet my mother remained forever determined to go back there and drag me with her. She craved the ease and affability of that submissive, dutiful daughter again. It showed in the offense she took when I wouldn't drink booze with her. Or in her irritation because I favored wearing skirts, when she'd accuse me of being *too good* to wear jeans like she did, when in fact I was ashamed that I couldn't get jeans big enough to cover my backside.

My growing modesty stuck in her craw. Blame it on Marriage Encounter, finding Jesus, or just the simple fact of raising daughters, but I'd long outgrown my taste for degrading sexual innuendoes and crude dirty jokes. I guess I'd become too much of a goody-two-shoes for my mother's liking, and to *knock me down a few pegs,* she threatened to hire male strippers to show up at my workplace—a galaxy of expensive suits, designer dresses, and extravagant perfumes encased in an atrium of sunlight and tropical plantings—just to embarrass me.

She would try to engage me in venomous gossip. When that failed, she inundated me with what I labeled "dead baby" stories she'd gleaned from the tabloids. Detailed accounts of children suffering inconceivable horrors. Among them, a child burn victim the headlines dubbed "The Crisco Kid" for how the nurses had to rub his charred toddler body down with Crisco vegetable shortening.

I felt like I needed to douse myself in holy water when I was around my mother. I had a husband who patrolled the unpredictable streets of a blighted, urban city with a badge and a gun that was no match for the weapons carried around by the lawless. And two young daughters I worried constantly about keeping safe from all manner of atrocities. And there was my mother, continually yanking me toward her craziness, evoking horrific images in the refuge of my kitchen with no regard for its emotional impact on me or our children. Pestering me to be the accommodating, commiserating daughter/companion that I was all those years ago.

My mother's relentless battle to revert me back to that compliant, faceless girl exhausted me. Frightened the hell out of me. Her silent tantrums; her anger; hysterics; obsession with misery, pain, and death; her suicide threats—all made my adult life a living hell.

Stopping for a moment now to reflect on the details that she revealed about her sister Bobby, I'm beginning to understand...

18

Patsy

I made *her* life a living hell? Did Kathleen tell you that she went out and got herself pregnant when she was a teenager? Did she tell you that her father and I had to *sell our house* and move away because of her? Did she tell you she almost *killed* her father because of *what she did*? She didn't tell you any of that, did she?

I made her life hell? Who the hell does she think she is after all I did for her when she got in trouble?

19

Kathleen

It was rape.

10

Patsy

Rape? **RAPE?**

I DIDN'T KNOW THAT.

IT'S NOT MY FAULT!

I DIDN'T KNOW ANY OF THAT.

WHY DIDN'T SHE TELL ME?

SHE SHOULDA TOLD ME.

IT'S HER FAULT FOR NOT TELLING ME.

IT'S NOT MY FAULT!

Kathleen

Kathleen *Barbara.* What was my mother thinking, naming me after her sister who repeatedly raped her? Barbara the rapist also happens to be my godmother. Being chosen godmother is a sacred honor. It confirms all kinds of wonderful things about the chosen: faithful Catholic; high moral values; trustworthy; no meat on Friday; confession on Saturday; Mass on Sunday and holy days of obligation. Basically, a walking saint. In Catholic world, Aunt Barbara—Bobby, as she was known—would be responsible for overseeing my spiritual development forevermore. That's some sick irony right there. I'm figuring my unwed teenaged mother either was a saint herself or eroded down to desperate measures, the last vestiges of human emotional survival.

You couldn't catch Bobby in a dress. Baggy trousers and men's flannel shirts were her uniform. But had you been around on the day of my Christening, you would've witnessed a miracle. And I'm not talking about the sacrament of baptism. According to the 8x10 black and white preserved for all time, Bobby donned a dress for the occasion—a feminine number that draped softly over her rounded curves. To be clear, it wasn't her choice—a woman in pants was not permitted in church, never mind a glaring dyke done up in jeans with a pack of Camels rolled up in her sleeve.

In the same photograph, my mother wears pearls and a delicate, short-sleeved sweater. Staring down at me swaddled in my mother's arms, both sisters look funeral grim. They are clearly avoiding the camera. No eye contact with the lens. No saying cheese. No striking a pose. Absent are the loving gazes and silly smiles I would expect, since I look so adorable all bundled up cocoon-like in a baptismal white blankie. And after all, I'd just been purified—purged of original sin brought on by those two troublemakers, Adam and Eve, who couldn't keep their hands off each other. Plus, from that day forward, should I succumb to a dastardly infant malady, I was saved from damnation to Limbo, where all the dead pagan babies hung out crying for Jesus. *And* as long as I toed certain very strict lines, my soul would be forever safe in the bosom of Catholicism. It was party time. But on that sunny afternoon in September, although I had been cleansed of all transgressions against God and, according to legend, should've been sleeping peacefully in the halo of divine grace, I too am grim—my brow furrowed with fret and discomfort as if I am wedged between anger and loss. A rapist to the left. A rape victim to the right. And in the middle—me—a product of rape. Three females tethered by family and misfortunes. Taking the picture? Uncle Pornographer. Gauging from the look on my face, if my feet worked, I would've been out of there.

A photographer by trade, in the life that counted, Uncle Russ was a pornographer who got himself evicted from an entire state. The warning went that if he ever set foot in Florida again, his balls would be handed to him on a platter. The exact nature of Uncle Russ's pornographic shenanigans remains unclear, but evidently, his balls meant more to him than orange juice and sunshine since he hightailed it back to New Jersey, genitals intact.

An uncle on their daddy's side, Russ was a puny, squirrelly man known for creeping along the shadowed edges of the family circle. There he was: a pervert with a camera and easy access. It's no wonder that there's a mood of female inertia embedded in that photograph. As if the sisters can barely tolerate the moment: the presence of Uncle Pornographer, of each other, of the charade. And can't wait for it to pass. The lens—Uncle Russ's private eye—undressing them. Scrutinizing me. Betraying secrets. The hidden entanglement of flesh and brutality. Evildoers and crimes. Innocence and ruin. The irreparable. The unsalvageable. The ghost of inescapable tragedy, bearing down like a train heading toward its wreck. All captured in an innocent family photograph shot on that sacred day in the middle of a perfect autumn afternoon.

22

Kathleen

By the time Bobby had finished raping her, every one of my mother's female boundaries had been pulverized, including her voice. All her good words had been killed off. What was left was dust. And since dust is about as effective for warding off aggressors as crucifixes are for defanging vampires, any power Patsy might have had to fight off sexual predators had been crushed beneath the pounding of Bobby's fists on the stinking sheets in that upstairs bedroom of the family homestead.

Patsy might as well have painted herself a big red sign announcing herself PREY and slung it around her neck like a billboard. All any predator needs is a whiff of weakness gliding on a gentle wind. One iota of blood in vast waters. A faint limping of the heart. The distinct, heady perfume of *conquest in the making* to happen by. That's all it took: one beaten-down girl and one rapist with a nose for his trade. Then along I came, the added outrage to Patsy's catastrophic sexual injuries. Sure I was as cute as a wrinkled puppy, but cute can't make up for female slaughter. Sure Bobby stepped up and feigned sainthood, but deception never erases destruction.

Right about now, I imagine that all those goody-goodies holed up merrily in "Disneyland" are reeling in shock. Recoiling at such talk. At the mere mention of secret perversions. *Family* perversions. Pornography. And rape. Rape committed by *family*. Rape committed *by a sister. A broken girl impregnated by rape.* The goody-goodies have a way of flaring their nostrils in disgust when they detect something putrid befouling their sanitary world, don't they? Wouldn't they be scandalized, then, by all the sexual rot floating through the breeze swaying the palm trees surrounding their manicured lawns? Where my family history tells me that beneath the heavy fronds, Uncle Pornographer amused himself with the sexually wounded?

23

Kathleen

I am not welcome in "Disneyland." Nor was my mother. No bleeding, sexually wounded woman is permitted entry into the Disneyland world of the goody-goodies with its sparkling fresh air fragranced so with magic. We are dirty. Stained. The air we breathe so befouled. Putrid. Contaminated. And oh, how the world of the sexually wounded is so very deprived of enchantment. Our ugliness offends Disneyland itself. We tarnish the twinkling lights and glittering sequins.

We are not fools. This is not news to us. But our hearts still love. We want what you want—smiles that don't reek lechery; to be comforted by words, not degraded; kind hands reaching out, not balled-up fists in our faces; safe refuge from stalkers declaring war on our sexual body parts; protection from vultures and predators declaring entitlement to our very being—except *we* are frantic. We don't know the why. Or the "how" of all that happened to us. All we know is Disneyland with its dedication to the immaculate, and the goody-goodies with their devotion to perfection.

Turned away from our home, we will die, fall to the crusty earth, and shrivel beneath the stone weight of banishment. So we pay whatever price necessary to stay inside the fairytale gates. We slather on theatrical makeup to hide our oozing wounds. We squeeze into whimsical costumes to conceal our filth and prettify our unutterable sins. We drive ourselves to near insanity, bleaching and cleansing the rancid air that envelops us, permeates us. We resolve to exterminate the rot with self-hatred, petrified denials, holy beads, and numbing substances before any goody-goody gets a whiff of our stink that is us.

We fail. Cue the manic urges of survival: endless compulsions that must be rigorously obeyed, chanted, and performed—feverish, last-ditch efforts aimed at lessening the insidious, lingering stench; our pathetic stabs at soothing the always-cruising, slobbering beasts stalking us, the shuffling, sexually wounded souls. Because unlike the amusing beastly characters parading down a fantasy Main Street, the beasts haunting our world are not imaginary—they are real, and they parade freely unseen in our homes, in our families, in our communities, in our spirits.

These beasts know our names. They prowl our dreams. Take delight in our weaknesses. They take our pictures. Attend our celebrations. They eat our food. They phone us. Send us Hallmark cards. They ingratiate themselves with the *good* citizens of Disneyland, faking kindness, confusion, and decency while stabbing us with cryptic daggers. These beasts do not die in death. They remain ensconced in sentimental family lore while smirking at us from ancient photos. Their ghosts taunt us with sly, cold-blooded whispers while the goody-goodies blather on and on, mourning their passing and praising their charms. These beasts don't leave us. Not ever. Not ever. Not ever. *Not ever.*

Kathleen

Bobby was not going anywhere. Her ass was firmly planted in that house in Fieldsboro. A beaten-down, impregnated, unmarried, teenaged Patsy had no place to go. But if she wanted to stay in the family Disneyland, it would cost her. The price was her life. Patsy would have to curl herself into a ball, admit defeat, and appease the enemy. Her body would have to assume the feat of living dolled up in the glittery costumes forced on her by the goody-goodies.

What was my mother thinking, naming me after her sister who repeatedly raped her? That's just it, she wasn't thinking. Panic doesn't think—it reacts. Like any drowning victim, Patsy was thrashing to survive. She ached to be immaculately clean, to live in a sparkling-bright world. She hungered for a magical storybook ending in the Disneyland where she was trapped. What she got was Sister Bobby and Uncle Russ.

25

Patsy

i can't move

26

Patsy

they through me in the river i was only eight

27

Patsy

I didn't know what Bobby done to me was rape. I don't know what to do now. I didn't know a lezzie could rape nobody. I never did think like Kathleen thinks. I can't hardly get the picture of what my daughter's talking about—Bobby killing my words. I don't have no good words to think things like she does.

28

Patsy

What if Kathleen's right? About Bobby? About lezzie rape and all that? I know that people can beat the shit out of you, but I never heard that people can beat the words out of you. I never thought about any stuff like that.

It stands to reason though, don't it? I never did have no good words. Not even with all them books I read…

Do you think Bobby raped me?

29

Patsy

About the other thing. That thing with Kathleen. Me having her. I *told* her that her father was her father. Me and her father, Jack, were married. I told her that. *I told her that. I told her that.* She's wrong about anything different! She's wrong! I swear on a stack of Bibles. I never said no different until the day I died. Now I'm dead. I still won't say no different. Nothin' else happened. Not nothin'. Jack and I were married. *Kathleen is his daughter.* Nothin' happened. Nothin'.

Jack loved Kathleen.
He loved her.
*He took her in...*I didn't mean that. *I didn't mean that.*

30

Patsy

I wish to God that *you* would burn in hell. I wish to God you were dead. Who do you think you are? If Jack was here right now, he'd kick the shit out of you. He wouldn't take this crap. You're nothin' but a damn hypocrite. You can catch a thief, but you can't catch a liar. You're worse than a lyin' hypocrite—you're a lyin' thief. You're taking everything away from me that I ever had. I got nothin' left. I got nothin'. I got nothin'.

I hope you rot in hell.

31

Patsy

It's not my fault that I get so mad sometimes and can't stop myself from hollering. I ruined a lot of things over hollering like I do. I don't know why people put up with me. I can't stand myself. I'm getting awful tired. Once my mind starts going, it don't stop. I wish I could make it stop, but I can't. All I can think about is Sister Bobby…

I never slept those nights in Bobby's bed. I was so cold…ice cold. I remember shivering like I had Saint Vitus's Dance. I remember squeezing myself into the wall and not moving the whole night. I'd listen to Bobby snore and pray she would die. I remember crying and screaming—but only to myself. I kept quiet. I had to lie there and not move a muscle so she wouldn't wake up. I'd pray the rosary in my head. But it didn't do no good.

I remember the bruises. I could *feel* them swelling up. I could feel them getting purple. All night they would throb and throb. I felt like my whole body had a toothache. I felt black and blue *down there*. I felt burning in places I don't have no words for. Like I had blisters inside me.

I remember how Bobby stank. How the bed stank. The sheets stank. The blankets stank. I *stank*. I didn't have no choice. I had to lie there smelling *her*. Smelling myself—smelling the horseshit stink of my queer sister smeared all over me. I had to wait until morning. I wouldn't move until I heard Mother downstairs in the kitchen. Then I'd rush down. I remember crying when I saw her in her housedress and apron standing at the oven, but I didn't let her see. I'd just scrub myself with lye soap and freezing well water. "Patsy," Mother would say, "The water will be warm in a few minutes." I couldn't wait for it to heat up on the stove. I made believe I liked the cold water. I'd scrub and scrub myself until I was raw, but I couldn't get clean. For my whole life, I couldn't get clean enough.

I'd like to smack Bobby right in her stinkin' ugly horse face. I hope she's rotting in hell.

32

Patsy

Nobody cares about an old woman. Nobody cares about what happened to an old woman. Nobody. It don't matter now anyhow. I'm so mad at myself for opening my big mouth and talking about all this that I could scream bloody murder. I'm stupid and ugly. I hate myself. Being dead don't change that. Nobody cares about an old dead woman.

Besides, I don't know what kind of bug Kathleen's got—I'd say up her ass, but I know she don't go in for that kind of talk. But she shoulda left well enough alone. Bringin' up all that stuff. I'm not saying one more damn word. Who cares about an old dead woman anyway?

33

Kathleen

Anyone spotting my mother's right wrist could not have missed those jagged, angry gashes buffed into spiteful cords of roping fused to her skin. Though for my entire life, not once did I hear anyone question the disfigurement, not even in whispered curiosity. But for as long as I've had working eyeballs, those thick, visible scars cried out to me like shiny, pale ghosts scoffing at her explanation for their presence on the delicate underside of her forearm. The more she kept to her story, the louder the ghosts cried. The louder the ghosts cried, the more agitated I became. So again and again, I'd pester her.

What happened to your wrist, Mommy?
Nothin', she'd say.
Or:
I smashed my fist through a window.
Why?, I'd ask.
Because I was mad.
Why?
I was just mad, that's all.

God, I must have made her nuts, always staring and badgering her about that crosshatch of scarring, but it looked so out of place on her. And for some unidentifiable reason—something akin to a vague tingle alerting to the onset of a nasty virus—that ugly marring protested her excuse. Every time she repeated her stale, stock answer—*I smashed my fist through a window*—it crawled across my skin like fire ants. I *wanted* to believe her. I *tried* to believe her. So again and again, I'd ask, *What happened, Mommy?* I'd squeeze my brain into a tight knot of concentration and listen intently to her words as they tumbled toward me, all the while battling to ignore the undertone of desolation and hum of disembodied hopelessness buffeting me with shockwaves of volcanic air. That agitated, fugitive concussion I could *sense* but couldn't *see* riled craziness in me.

What I couldn't see rippled like noiseless globs beneath the scum of scalding milk as I waited for the satisfying boil. I could *almost* see the whorls and kinks wiggling, readying to churn the milk into a caldron of furious bubbles, merely to dissipate back down into the pot seconds before breaking through the creamy surface. Outwitting my eye. Escaping detection. Try trapping a tease of candlelight flickering across a skeleton. Or chasing an echo braying in the deserted woods, only to have it erupt somewhere else as a turbulent bellow to again mock me with its phantom, primal presence.

I wanted to believe her. I'd pull my mother's words into my head, where I could examine them for rhyme and cadence, where I could measure their weight and make them fit. If I could just set things in order—line up all her words and all the spooky stuff properly; convince myself that I was simply possessed of nothing more than a morbid, overdramatic imagination—then the truth of my mother smashing her fist through a conveniently located window would settle down peacefully, and the bothersome mental fire ants and disembodied echoes would vanish into an abyss. And serenity would reign. Then I could read the truth of her scars like an A$^+$ book report, take it to heart for its accuracy, and finally be done with it. And relax and author grisly fairytales to assuage my magnetism to the macabre.

But I couldn't catch vapor. The second my mother uttered *I smashed my fist through a window,* her words fell flat—listless and stagnant. And needled me like poison ivy with a bad attitude. And there I'd be with a flaming itch I was crazed to scratch but couldn't reach. And anxiety I couldn't contain. What else could I do? I had to hover. Close enough to touch her skin. Close enough to be caressed by the comforting scent of bleach and cigarette smoke. Close enough to keep watch. Close enough to save her should she fall. Close enough to hold her back from the void that beckoned her with long, gnarled fingers. Since at any given moment my mother could disappear forever into the vast gloom of her shadows.

And along with her, she would take my soul. I would hear her cries. I would hear my own. But in the terrifying dark, all cries are useless.

A lifetime has now passed. Here I am, an old woman, my mother dead, and still I am imprinted by the ghostly wail of those scars on her wrist. *The ghostly wail.* It sounds so Stephen King. So horror movie. So ghost hunters on the search for the dementedly departed. Except those scars are ghosts casting candlelight across a skeleton, braying in the deserted woods. Those wailing ghosts are not the sinister hauntings of my discombobulated mind—they bear a tragic, human story and taunt with glimpses of silhouettes in the mist, shapes I can't quite make out.

I am certain now that those scars deliberately spilled surreal light across the visceral darkness of the leaking wounds of the soul, wailing to be listened to. It has taken me a lifetime to hear. A lifetime for the memory to emerge from the haze.

I remember now. I remember now the wails of a broken young woman begging to die. And I remember now my shrieks—the shrieks of a helpless, infant witness.

34

Patsy

I don't know what Kathleen's talking about. I told her a million times: *I smashed my fist through a window because I was mad.* That's all. I was just mad. Why the hell does she keep going on about all this stuff?

35

Kathleen

Allow me to wax poetic about my mother. Oh my gosh, she was my beautiful, blessed mother. As far as I was concerned, she floated around on a cloud, and I longed... *longed*... to float right next to her, gripping her hand. If I could've been sewn into her apron pocket—a weird, tiny joey of the human variety—my life would've been blissfully and forever complete. Not that I was as cute as a kangaroo. Hardly. Too many Toni Home Permanent Waves had forced perfectly good hair into crispy tangles of steel wool. And flab the size of a spare tire hugging my middle would've looked a whole lot better on Porky Pig. Nobody ever called me a tub of lard, but that's how I felt.

As little girls go, besides being chubby, I was horribly bashful, easily frightened, and—due to rabid self-consciousness—given to clumsy ties of the tongue. What kid wants to stand paralyzed while her tongue ties itself into unnatural knots when asked to produce a few coherent words, then have to endure fever rushing to her cheeks like flames chasing after a fire? I spent my entire youth as a living thermometer, helplessly broadcasting my deficiencies with varying shades of crimson. I never confessed, but there was a reason for all this blushing. One word: terror. Wedged somewhere in the center of my chest was an encyclopedia's worth. My world was fraught with dangers I alone could see.

The worst of the worst? Social encounters with strangers. *I deplored strangers.* The worst of the worst of the worst? Men strangers. Men did not have hearts. And since men were heartless, all men—whether I knew them or not—qualified as strangers, including my father. Without my mother at my side, every social encounter with a man was white-knuckle terrifying. It was the eyes—they menaced me. Nothing stirred there. Too much stirred there. Men's eyes had this way of peering through my clothes and devouring my girl privacies. And while their eyes were busy with debauchery, their mouths battered me with nonsense—*What grade you in? You're "big" for your age, aren't ya? Where'd you get those bedroom eyes? Bet you got a boyfriend, doncha?*—or held to rigid silence. I could feel their cold blood rummaging through my insides, looking. Poking. Spoiling for a reaction. *Cat got your tongue, huh? Huh? Huh?* Any reaction at all. Thanks to my tied tongue and pyrotechnic theatrics, I didn't disappoint.

Trapped in a maelstrom of condoned adult-male-on-young-girl aggression, my fevered cheeks betrayed my weakness and always fed the beast. No matter that my nerves revolted and zapped every living cell with electrical volts. Igniting my danger instinct. Detonating the alarm to *immediately* ABANDON SHIP! ABANDON SHIP! Enforced good manners forbid any notion of fleeing. I *had* to stay. And be courteous. Stay and stammer. Stay and endure. Stay and smile. Stay and blush. And blush. Redder. And redder. Stay until the man-stranger got bored or distracted and I could melt away quietly. Or my mother calmly rescued me.

My mother was my only protection, the buffer between me and *them*. She provided the diversion, charmed men with her feisty beauty, absorbed their monkey business without employing it as weaponry against me. Her presence was the only place where I could breathe in safety. Where I didn't have to worry. Or look over my shoulder. Where the knobs of anxiety melted into liquid satin. Where I could rest. And dream my dreams.

I guess I was one of those kids only a saint could love. And tolerate. I've seen toddlers screech at the disappearance of their mommies even if the poor woman just slipped into the bathroom for a smoke. I was one of those kids. I worshiped my mother. I followed her. I inhaled her. This tightly wound love—*wherever you go, let me go too*—lasted long, long past babyhood. So long I am embarrassed to say. Eventually I stopped screeching—out loud, anyway. I just fretted. I'd clamp my lips between my teeth, pull tight worry lines across my brow, and sob—hysterically and mutely—while violent images of my mother vanishing into thin air flashed across my mind: behind the closed bathroom door, the big flush would swallow her alive and she would be forever gone; she would be killed in a car crash, consumed by fire and molten steel, never to be seen again; the cops would mistake her for a criminal and drag her off to jail, leaving me to fend for myself in a world made crude and unsafe by vulgar strangers. All this is why, if I could have managed it, I would've lodged myself inside my mother's pocket. Permanently.

I don't understand all the ways of terror. But I know of its entrenched roots and strangling vines and the wake it leaves behind—pain deep enough to drown in and puzzles too formless to solve. My mother dying was *real* to me. The visions. The sensations. Its premonition. The fear of her death was a living, breathing savage that had the power to terrorize me at the nod of a distant wind. I *felt* her impending death. I *heard* its whisper. I recoiled from its heckling. It was as if a long-forgotten voodoo curse had been hand-carved onto the underside of my heart in symbols divined from gibberish going back to a time beyond my recall. When spoken language was just a jumble of rising pitch and falling tones, and vision a blur of attacking images. Manic intuitions of confusion and turbulence—vivid impressions; piercing, explosive voices; deafening noise—taunted me, hammered me with frantic undertones, but bore no word story. Even now, with so many years dissolved behind me, sounds and images of maternal mayhem and danger still flash phantom warnings in my head and trigger stabbing alerts inside my gut. I sense *something*. I'm just not sure what.

And then the memory drifts up as soft as a dream. And I know. *I know...*

36

Kathleen

Soothing, familiar voices rise in sudden, frenzied panic. Sobbing ... I hear sobbing. Just below my milky slumber. Wrenching, choking sobs. Faces contorted and purpled—hollering, threatening—flit around me like nightmares flashing through turbulent mist. Fright takes shape and descends like a fiend to snatch me from the safety of my nap. I startle awake—arms and legs thrashing—flinching from the sting of static electricity crackling and snapping, arcing through the spaces between the slats. Thundering shouts. Pounding feet race across floorboards—the muffled wop-wops of scurrying footfalls. The floor beneath me, under the playpen, flexes and contracts. Flexes and contracts. My full belly stiffens. I flail and wriggle, trying to shrink away from the airborne assault. But my round body at once freezes and convulses as disjointed images pounce and swoop at me like strange bullets from an angry gun. It is pandemonium. Chaos I cannot make sense of.

Until in the midst of the bedlam emerges a gamy odor that uncoils a thread and links me to something familiar. A smell that I recognize from before. And goo I recall but cannot name. Over there. All over her. All over my mother. Wet. Sticky. Dark. Terrifying.

I am shrieking.

37

Kathleen

There is a *knowing* that glides in like breath and settles into the heart and breaks it. This knowing, the magnitude of it, renders me nearly speechless. My mother. A teenager. Plundered. Raped. Impregnated. Brutally betrayed by her trusted Catholic God—a turncoat. I know well that turncoat Catholic God. He lives in my own history as a treacherous, insatiable savage beast that rages and taunts defiled girls incessantly. Unmercifully.

What else would her savage Catholic God do except whip my mother until she was unable to draw a breath that wasn't ripped to pieces as it chattered across her gaping anguish. Until she was dismantled. Until the blade of a razor glinted with the halo of a savior. And flesh yielded to gore as she slit her wrist clear down to the bone. To erase herself and to appease the savage Catholic God.

That kind of chaos imprints on a kid, no matter how young. It is a fierce suspension of dark vapor concealed in the wild-eyed viscera, a place I cannot point to. Yet it preserves that day of blood for me: all the crying and yelling; the lurching floorboards; the wet, sticky, dark goo eerily remembered from the solemn day of my birth, splattered everywhere. Somehow the ghost of that chaos hunkered way down like an unseen bruise evermore to hold me prisoner within its swollen, primitive warp that pulsates—bloating and tightening—according to its own whim.

By way of natural sorcery, I—the infant witness—documented that gruesome, bygone incident frame by frame, sequestering it in the wilderness of my nerves and vitals where it bred sinister visions shouting prophecies of doom that haunted me and made me cling to my mother long past what's considered rational.

Because I *saw* what no one else could see. I *remember* my mother as a mangled lump of blood and collapsed bones. I saw my mother dying. The infant witness *knows*. And still shrieks, cursed with terror.

38

Patsy

I told Kathleen a million times: I was *mad*—I don't remember at what—and I just smashed my fist through a window. *I always had a rotten temper.* That's all. I smashed my fist through a window. That's all. I was mad. I don't remember at what. *How many damn times do I have to say it so she'll believe it?* I smashed my fist through a window.

That's all. I was mad. I don't remember at what. I smashed my fist through a window.

That's all. I was mad. I don't remember at what. I smashed my fist through a window.

That's all. I was mad. I don't remember at what. I smashed my fist through a window.

That's all. I was mad. I don't remember at what. I smashed my fist through a window.

That's all. I was mad. I don't remember at what. I smashed my fist through a window.

That's all. I was mad. I don't remember at what. I smashed my fist through a window.

That's all. I was mad. I don't remember at what. I smashed my fist through a window.

How many damn times do I have to say it?

39

Pat

I sliced my wrist with a razorblade.
I didn't smash my fist through a window.
I sliced my wrist with a razorblade.

40

Pat

Damn it! *I didn't ram my fist through a window. I sliced my wrist with a razorblade.* Are you happy now? Well, I hope to hell Kathleen is, now that she forced me to talk. Words kill you. They used to cut people's tongues out for talking, you know that? Is that what she wants to happen to me? It'll be all her fault if it does. I'm going to have to pay for all this. For all that crap I said about my sister. For telling about the razor. They kill women for talking. I'll be killed even deader than I am now. And I won't have nothin' left. I'm going to have to pay for everything I say. And I blame Kathleen for making me talk. Women go to Hell for things. For saying things. For doin' things. It don't make no difference that I'm already dead.

I need a cigarette. Damn it. That's the least you could do. Get me a cigarette.

41

Pat

Nobody cared. Nobody cared. I wanted to die. I wanted to bleed to death. I remember a lot of blood. It could've filled a bucket. I was happy about that. *Happy.* I bled a bucket of blood. There was so much rumpus. All for me. Hollering. Confusion. Thumping. I think it was heavy shoes running across the wood floors. I was woozy. They all rushed to me. Mother. Daddy. One of my brothers, I think. Maybe Paul, the oldest. Somebody picked me up. Somebody strong. I was limp. Blood was everywhere. Red. Red. Red behind my eyes. All over my new blouse. Dripping down on my pants—ones like Carole Lombard wore—that I bought with tips from the bar and grill where I served drunks.

I heard shrieking. A baby? In the distance. Shrieking like an animal. A tiny little animal shrieking. And shrieking. I didn't care. I liked the blood. And the noise. All for me. All for me.

Are you satisfied now? You made an old lady cry.

42

Kathleen

I don't know where the expression "I could spit wooden nickels" actually originated. Given a guess, I'd have to say my mother coined it since she was the first and only person I've ever heard use that phrase. It held a respected place in her repertoire of anger responses, sandwiched right there between hostile silence and *I oughta beat the shit out of you.* Not that she'd get official credit, but she should. If only because of her one-woman devotion to its knack for instilling enough fear to get rambunctious kids laughing and on the run, greatly reducing the likelihood of having to chase us with a dust rag and threats about beatings and shit and all that. Alas, the wooden nickel saying seems to have died along with her. Now here I am resurrecting it from the dead. Because it fits. And because the satisfaction of throwing a temper tantrum with a raggedy undershirt saturated with furniture polish has been effectively undermined by the invention of the flimsy microfiber dust cloth. *And* these days you are not supposed to chase *anybody* around issuing threats about whippings and scaring bowels into embarrassing reactions.

But *spitting wooden nickels* fits. And that's what I could do right about now, spit wooden nickels. For my mother. For me. For all the silenced women of the past and those haunting the present. For future heirs to the legacy of family secrets and woman silence. Wait... Forget wooden nickels. I'm feeling hellfire and lead bullets.

So much of my mother's life, so much of my life, lost to lies. So much intelligence, creative force, so much vitality wasted, consumed by the non-stop work of *trying* to belong. Pretending that we weren't hounded by the darkness of guilt and shame. Decades upon decades of exhaustive energy squandered on tiptoeing, slump-shouldered, among the disdainful. Hiding and cowering from those who would condemn us. Trying not to stink of sin. Straining to pass for "normal." Fighting. Fighting to uphold the lies we believed safeguarded us. Battling—battling the invisible tsunami of terror when the lies we believed were divinely sent for our protection turned on us. Reduced us to prey. Forced us to run even as our bodies stood rigid, frozen in place. Drove our hearts into the void. Filled us with fear. And rage. When all that we longed for, martyred ourselves for, begged for, was peace, joy, and happiness—the blessings of Christmas. Blessings available to all. But not to my mother. Not to me. Because of…because of…*what happened. What we did. What we failed to do.* Because *it* was our fault. Whatever *it* was, we were to blame and we *knew it.* Because a woman fouled and branded by mortal sin—as set forth by all who sit in judgment—is forever its prisoner, forever stigmatized. My mother cultishly believed this. As did I.

We *believed* in the anger of Heaven. *Believed* in God's enthusiasm for punishment. Believed in our offensiveness. To God. To others. To the Holy Catholic Church. Therefore, we *believed* that by ritually vilifying ourselves—wrenching our gentle hearts out of our own aching chests, blackening our sweet, tender souls with self loathing, crawling and pleading in utter subordination, and offering it all up as blood-spattered sacrifice for glorification and appeasement—then God might, *might* grant us some sort of mercy. That is what my mother did. And schooled by her, what I did. Fervently. Secretly. Privately. We implored. Prayed. Bargained. Behind closed doors, we knelt at the edge of our beds clutching prayer cards— St. Anthony, St. Joseph, St. Jude of lost causes—crying out for their intercession. Our faces buried in freshly laundered bedspreads. Sobbing. Fanatically reciting the rosary. Two, three, four times a day. However many times necessary to gain favor of the Blessed Mother. So she might petition her Son to grant pity on us. Faithfully and blindly, we followed the lethal order for silence and secrecy. So that the angry trinity—God, the cantankerous Father in Heaven; his moody, ever-suffering Son at His right hand; and the nosy Holy Ghost that scrutinized every single damn moment of every single damn day—would bestow upon us…What? Safety for our loved ones? Yes! The skill to vanish? To live unnoticed in the background? Yes! Yes! Exactly! To please let us not be noticed. To *please, please* keep our sins private—*Oh Lord, we beg of you, grant us invisibility. Lord, we beseech thee for a safe place to hide. We implore you, Holy Queen, Mother of Mercy, please erase us from view. Amen. Amen. Amen.* Neither my mother nor I had any comprehension that we were praying for the death of our souls.

Those scars on my mother's wrist are none of my business. But the story is not the scars. The story is the lie. The lie was the living, malevolent force. The lie was the breathtaking hatred my mother directed at herself. Diminishing herself with every telling. Passively accepting its malignant command over her spirit. Dutifully complying with the murder of her own soul. Never daring to doubt the lie's capacity to defend her. Never considering the idiocy of its exalted guarantee to protect her forever. Never recognizing, even as she tottered along on frail nerves, that it was the lie—not the incident—that kept her trapped in emotional chaos. The lie is what whipped itself up into a frenzy. Bounced off the walls. Stabbed me with lightning strikes. Snatched away my own breath. Kept at me. And at me. Until I couldn't keep my mouth shut. And I nagged. And pestered. Trying to shake loose its grip so I could breathe.

Maybe if my mother had pointed to her wrist and said, "Kathleen, you see this? It's none of your business. It's mine. And that's how it's going to stay. You're being rude and disrespectful. Don't ask me again. I'm *not* going to talk about it. This conversation is over." *Okay, then.* I get it. Boundary set. Not that I would've been happy. Bring out the wooden nickels. But I would've known to keep my mouth shut, my belligerent curiosity to myself. Her message would have rung loud and clear: *mind your own business. This is my final warning. My line in the sand. Cross over it and you lose.* The voice of a woman who's had enough kid nonsense and now she's done. Mother as her own authority. Not mother as victim.

But that's not how it was. My mother built a steel cage of lies around herself. Only her lies leaked sorrow. I wish I could have managed compassion for the anger that accompanied her undercurrent of misery. But I didn't know how to get my blood to stop boiling when her behavior deteriorated into obnoxious territory. My mother lived by the law that nobody's pain mattered. Tears? *I'll give you something to cry for.* Blood?

Stop bleeding. There was simply no way to know that although she was a grown woman, my mother bore the inflamed, permanent scarring of an emotionally damaged little girl. I couldn't feel her heart. I couldn't see past the maddening racket she created with the intensity of a rebellious kid refusing to stop banging her fists on an out-of-tune piano. I just thought she was hateful.

I never imagined her shrunken and lost, a ghost child struggling inside a sad entanglement of longing and self destruction, desperately craving love and approval. I only saw what she showed: deliberate and fierce determination to sabotage any attempt to draw in close to her. Anyone daring enough to offer her tenderness was met with cold, flippant defiance. Once I complained, *I know there's a heart in there somewhere.* She never forgave me for that misstep of frustration that must have burned like a blade thrust into a weeping ulcer. Her lies protected the buried, festering wound of love; forbid access to the raw, well-hidden bunker where her tears flowed nonstop. I understand that now.

I recall how she tried never to falter. Tried always to appear dangerous and independent, a woman you didn't want to mess with. But sometimes she'd trip. And inadvertently I'd see the shame she so ferociously fought to keep concealed. See her trying to build herself up in the eyes of others with what she wanted to be true. But wasn't. And never would be. See how she was stripping herself naked without even knowing it. And my heart would sink. If my mother knew how her lies mocked her—how they exposed her—she would have been mortified.

Even as age gathered on her back, collapsed her spine, and grew a hump there, still my mother kept up her lies. Invented new ones. Trying her best to promote the Pat of her dreams. The Pat that she wanted everyone to see. Determined not to expose herself, to stay safely hidden. Lest she be *accused*...of unpardonable sins...of being disgusting...of being too stupid to be bothered with. Then *rejected* and *shunned*—by her family, by strangers, by those in authority over her—for her imperfections and failures.

Long long ago, lies baited a trap for my mother—a young woman tormented by trauma—luring her in with soothing promises of rescue and freedom. Only to enslave her. Force her to construct her own psychological slum. And to abandon herself there to exist in utter isolation. With no hope of escape.

There from that place — disconnected from herself, separated from her soul, left to wander about in endless fear — my mother severed all connection with her own goodness. Spurned love. Burned bridges. And spit useless wooden nickels.

43

Patsy

Big deal. *Spit wooden nickels.* You think now that I'm dead all I have to do is spit stupid wooden nickels? You, dum-dum, are sadly mistaken. I have to watch out for myself around here. That's why I didn't go to the light. I'm nobody's fool. They keep trying to tell me I have privileges. That's what it's called on this side: *privileges.* They tell me I have the *privilege* to speak. That's a laugh. I don't have no good words. Besides, I hate women who talk too much. Most women don't have nothin' to say. That light's not gonna make me talk. It makes me think of *Dragnet* with...what's his name? Jack Webb. Tryin' to get a murderer or some thief to confess. *Just the facts, ma'am. Just the facts.* Anyhow, I don't have nothin' to say worth listening to.

And stop asking me stupid questions. *Yes, I see the light. How the hell could I miss it? It's always there. It's drivin' me to drink the way it keeps trying to rope me in.* I could float up there right this minute and dive in. But I heard that lie before. *C'mere, Patsy. C'mon. Just dive, Patsy. Just dive in. There's nothing to be scared of.* You think I'm a dum-dum like you? Just because I'm dead doesn't mean I'm stupid. They almost drowned me in the Delaware. And again in that sewer, Gropp's Lake. Yeah, *Just dive, Patsy.* Yeah, *Dive into hell, Patsy*, they shoulda said.

I don't forget.

44

Patsy

I waited a long time to die. Eighty-four years, if you insist on being nosy. And I wouldn't give a dime for most of them. Something in me always wanted to die. How do I know what made me always want to kick the bucket? That's just the way I was. I told you I was ornery.

Now I come to find out bein' dead's not so great either. It's not what it's cracked up to be, and I'm pissed off about that. I wanted peace. I worked my fingers to the bone for a little peace. But it's not here. There's not much difference between here and where you are, except now that I'm dead, I can see things. I guess that's considered a *privilege* too, but I'm not going for it. Why do I want to *see* what I didn't want to know in the first place? Believe me, it's all crap.

I've had it with you. You think you know everything. You're trying to make me feel like I'm too scared to go into that light. I'm not scared of nothin'. Just because I *can* float around doesn't mean I'm going to. Don't I get a say in this? I don't need this shit. I don't need you. I don't need nobody. I lived my whole life alone. Did I say physically alone? No, I did not. I had a lot of people around me. Most of them I couldn't stand. But I wanted them around anyway. I wasn't alone when there was lots of people around. I could be somebody else. I could joke around. I could laugh with the best of them. That was when Jack was still alive. Things turned when he died. And now I'm dead and all I have here are headaches. Too damn many bad memories. And you poking around in them.

I'm gettin' real aggravated. I don't know why the hell I'm talking to you. *I hate talking.* My life is none of your damn business. I don't give a shit about that damn light, either. I'm glad I'm alone. That's how I want it, damn it. Finally, I don't have to kiss anybody's big fat backside. Wooden nickels, my ass.

45

Pat

Anyhow, who cares about an old woman? Who cares about what happened to an old woman? Nobody cares how an old woman feels. Why are you pestering a stupid, ugly old woman that nobody cares about? You don't care about me. You just want the dirt. I wish you'd leave me alone.

How would *you* like it if you sent your own mother to Hell like I did? Here I am, an 84-year-old dead woman, and I never got over sending my own mother to Hell. It wasn't my fault. But if I get caught admitting what I did—that I damned Mother, even though I did it by accident—I'll be in terrible trouble. Now go away.

46

Pat

I'm only telling you this because you're such a pest and you keep coming back. You're worse than a wart on my ass.

If you must know, all I did was ask Mother to hem my skirt. That's how I sent her to Hell. Are you happy now? It was a Sunday, and Catholics weren't allowed to do servile work on a Sunday. How was I supposed to know what servile work was? All I knew was that nobody was supposed to do *it*. But I never knew that servile work meant sewing or I wouldn't have asked Mother to hem my skirt. She didn't tell me about Hell until after she stuck the needle back in her pincushion and handed me my skirt to try on.

I was twirling around in front of the mirror like a ballet dancer. I loved to dance. The skirt looked so pretty. Then Mother said, "Oh Patsy, Mother's going to Hell after she dies to pay for doing servile work on Sunday." I remember freezing in mid-air. I looked like a dumb skinny scarecrow with my arms sticking straight out, watching my reflection in the mirror turn black as sin. "Every stitch Mother ever sewed on a Sunday, she's going to have to take out with her nose over and over when she dies. For all eternity." She sounded real sad.

I never told nobody this, but I cried about sending my own mother to Hell. I told Kathleen half the story. I acted like it was nothin'. I tried real hard to find some good words. Words that wouldn't say too much. Words that wouldn't give me away. I made it real short. I told it like a joke. I didn't look at her, but I was feeling for her eyes. Waiting to *feel* how she looked at me. I kept back what I really wanted to say though—how awful sorry I was that I sent my mother to Hell, how I cried about that, how I prayed and prayed for Mother's immortal soul. But them words I didn't dare say kept pushing inside my head so bad they gave me a headache. They sat in my mouth like throw-up. I had a real hard time keeping them in.

Then I took a chance. I didn't want to, but I did—I *looked* at Kathleen.

I remember my stupid heart beating so hard. Them stupid words poundin' in my head. I remember...I remember lookin' in Kathleen's eyes and thinkin' I was gonna see how ugly I was, how ugly she thought I was. But all I saw was...I dunno...somethin' I couldn't put my finger on. Somethin' nice. Somethin' that made me want to say more. But I kept my mouth shut. I got scared that she'd call me selfish and stupid for making Mother do my skirt up. I was scared she'd be real mad at me for sending my mother to Hell. Kathleen was always soft on my mother. It wouldn't matter if it was on purpose or by accident. I still did it.

God put a jinx on me because of that skirt. Because I never confessed that I made Mother do servile work on a Sunday. Because I condemned her to Hell. I wished to God I burned that skirt. I wish I tore it to shreds and threw it down the pit in the outhouse.

You think God didn't punish me over that skirt? You'll never know how bad I was punished. How much I cried.

47

Pat

I don't know what's happening to me. I don't know why I can't keep my mouth shut after all these years. If you woulda just left me alone, I wouldn't be forced to tell my thoughts. I'm never gonna forgive you for this. For making me *talk*. For making me *want* to talk. There are some names I could call you right now. Names that would make your head spin. Names you think old ladies don't know. Names you think old ladies don't use. You're the one that's dumb, thinkin' that old ladies are *nice*. I use *shit, ass, faggot, spic, nigger, twat, wop, piss,* and *goddamned* more times in one day than you heard your whole life. How do you like them apples? It's your fault for making me need to say them bad words.

But I'll tell you one thing: nobody can ever accuse me of using that other word. That word you and everybody else uses nowadays. That *F* thing. That's the dirtiest word in the book. You wouldn't catch me using that word if my life depended on it. That word will send you straight to Hell.

Damn it, you're not gonna get any more out of me. One day you're gonna wish being dead took away your memories. Mark my words — it don't. Then you'll know what it's like. Bein' dead's not for sissies.

Pat

I've been thinkin'. About Kathleen.

All I'm gonna say is that something about Kathleen always unnerved me. It was her eyes. Something in her eyes. They were deep or something. I don't have no good words. Blue eyes, but what you would call deep-set, I guess. Her father used to tease her about her eyes: *They're like deep pools*, he'd kid. Then he'd add: *like cesspools.* He got that from some song, I think. Or maybe a Marx Brothers movie. I can't remember. I don't know why he kept at her like he did, but her eyes *were* like deep pools. I can't say it no other way. It was weird the way they seemed to see into your skin. Like she was X-raying you. Sometimes I'd think she could read my thoughts. And I didn't want her to. No, I guess I *did* want her to. I wanted *somebody* to. I think I *let* her read my thoughts. But then I'd get mad.

When she was little, she'd run her small fingers under my wrist. That's where the scars are...*were.* Where I... *I already told you about that. Don't ask me again.* I couldn't stand to be touched, especially there. I'd just freeze, waiting for her to stop. Thinkin' that my head was gonna fall off my shoulders and I'd be dead, *finally.* She was so nice. I didn't know what to do. I didn't deserve it. I wasn't nobody. I was scared because she acted like I was somebody. Like I meant something to her. That's the only way I can tell it. Kathleen scared me because she was so nice to me. I didn't deserve all the ways she looked like she loved me. She smiled at me all the time. She always wanted to be near me. Nobody ever treated me like that. Before Kathleen, nobody ever loved me.

I can still feel her fingers running over my skin where it was real hard and shiny there on my wrist. I remember like it was yesterday. I remember it hurt. It still does, even though I'm dead. Hurt not like the pain when somebody hits you. Not like that. But it hurt in my heart. It made me want to cry. It made me want to run away, because I didn't deserve that kindness. I *let* her touch me. But I couldn't watch. I had to look away. Outside the window. At the sags in the couch. At my knickknacks lined up along the shelves in the kitchen. Anywhere but at Kathleen. Anything to distract me from her niceness.

I couldn't stand bein' loved.

Pat

Now, this is the *last* thing I'm gonna say. I don't even know why I'm talking to you. It's none of your business. I don't go in for memories. What good are they? They only hurt you. I hate my memories. Who'd want to remember what I been through? I'll tell you one thing: if I was young again, if I was starting out, I'd do things a hell of a lot different. I wouldn't have kids, for one thing.

I was *never* one for kids. I never made over them like some people did. You think that just because I didn't complain, I *enjoyed* changing shitty diapers on all those foster kids Mother crammed into the dining room? Don't you think I had things *I* wanted to do? You're nuts if you think I ever *wanted* kids of my own. I can't even stand talking to you, you're so dumb. You look at me, but you don't see nothin' but an old woman. I don't even know why I'm wasting my time with you. You don't wanna know nothin'.

But I'm gonna tell you one thing. I had a dream once. I never told that to nobody. I wanted to be a star, a real star. Like Shirley Temple. Mother and Daddy even let me take tap-dancing lessons. I can still feel my feet dancing. I can still hear my shoes tapping on the school stage. Mother used to set my hair in rags so I'd have banana curls. And then she'd fix me up with a real big pretty bow. And when I danced, the curls bounced in time with my feet. I loved it. I loved all of it. The music. The attention. All the clapping. It still gives me the chills. *I know that was a long time ago. I know I'm dead. You don't have to remind me!* I'm trying to tell you how I felt. *Nobody ever listens to me.*

When I was dancing, I didn't stink of baby spit-up. I didn't have a crying kid on my hip. I was a star. People cheered me. They called me "Little Patsy." They said how cute I was. The more they clapped, the harder I danced. I wanted them to keep clapping. I wanted to keep hearing nice things about myself. But it didn't last. Nothin' good lasted. Not Jack. Not Mother. They both left. Jack had the nerve to die. Mother just drove off.

50

Pat

Mother left.

It happened when I was little, but I'll never forget. I'll never forget the sun, how it made me sweat in my hair while I was waiting for Mother on the post office steps. I can remember how my arms stank—just like how my brothers smelled after they were roughhousing outside all day. I couldn't stand to sweat, but on that day I didn't mind. I sat in that hot sun, staring up the street. Then staring down the street. Waiting. Looking for Mother's car. I never moved. Not an inch. Not once the whole time. Not even when I got thirsty. I didn't talk to nobody. Not even the town clown, who tried to make me laugh by sticking out his tongue. I just kept staring down the street. Waiting. Staring and waiting. Letting the sweat drip. I didn't even bother to wipe it off.

I got so drowsy, like I was floating on the air. I think I musta fell asleep, because I started dreaming. Not really dreaming. *Remembering.* But the remembering was all wrapped up in hurt that felt like a bad cramp squeezing my heart. I don't have no words to say it no other way. The dream felt like a fuzzy, slow-motion movie that I was watching, only it wasn't make-believe like regular dreams.

51

Patsy

Mother takes a pencil. "Watch me, Patsy," she says, and draws lines on a big sheet of white paper. Thick lines. Letters. Words. She pulls me on her lap. She's soft and cozy. And smells like oatmeal. I like the way she whispers in my ear. Like she's telling me a secret. I want to be Mother's favorite. I listen hard in my head. "Trace the letters with your finger, Patsy, just like me."

I please her. I can feel her happiness right through her dress. I push my pointer finger around the lines real careful. I think so hard that my head shrinks into a little dot that I look out of. I pretend that I'm looking through my brother's telescope. I don't see nothin' but the letters. "Memorize the shapes, Patsy." I do. I do. I look up and see Mother smiling down at me. She looks like an angel in a snow globe. My heart beats real fast and I go back into the dot. I squint and stare at the letters through that dot.

What's Mother doing? Oh. She's tucking a slip of paper in my shoe and tying the laces real tight. Too tight. They pinch my ankle. But I don't care, because Mother whispers that I am her favorite — "Patsy dear," she calls me. I feel so happy. Like a glowing star. I am so special, Mother tells me, that she is giving me a special chore to do — a secret chore. "Don't tell Daddy," she whispers real quiet through the curls right next to my ear. "Just put it in your shoe, Patsy dear." The way she says them, her words sound like music. I make them into a song that I sing to myself. Put it in your shoe, Patsy dear, Patsy dear. Match the letters, Patsy dear, Patsy dear. Don't tell daddy, Patsy dear, Patsy dear.

I'm scared of the old lady. She has crooked fingers. My brothers say she's a witch and that if her claw touches me, I'll turn into a witch too. I don't like when my chest thumps so hard. I stand on tippy-toes and reach up as far as I can and try not to look at the claw. I close my eyes when she hands me the mail over the counter. I'm so afraid of that claw. She says, "Here you go, Patsy," and I run out of the post office without even saying thank you.

I need to sit down on the steps to do my tracing and matching, but I forgot about splinters! If I sit down, I'll get one, because the steps are wood. But I have to match and trace before I go home. Mother said! I don't know what to do! If I get a splinter, it'll hurt real, real bad. It'll get all red and pus-y. And Mother will have to dig it out with a big sewing needle. My eyes want to cry.

I try not to look at the barroom across the street. It's dark and spooky and gives me goose pimples every time I see it. Sometimes Daddy goes in there, and when he comes out, he acts funny. And he smells. I'm scared of the clown that lives in that barroom. I know he's a clown because he has a red nose and he yodels and he falls down a lot. One time he said, "Give me a hand, will ya, Patsy?" I ran away. What if the clown comes out and waves at me and starts yodeling and falls down again and says, "Give me a hand, will ya, Patsy?" What'll I do? What'll I do? My brothers laugh at him, but he makes my eyes want to cry.

Oh no! I just remembered—the hairy man-baby! I spin around in a great big circle looking for man-baby and his mother and I almost drop the mail. What if his mother pushes him right up to these steps in his baby buggy? How will I run away with all this mail and only one shoe on? What if she makes me come over to the buggy and say hi to man-baby because doesn't he look so cute today wrapped up in his little blue blanket? What if she makes me mind man-baby while she gets her mail?

Mother told me that it's not man-baby's fault that he has a mustache. And if it wasn't for his beard, man-baby would look a lot like Clark Gable. Anyway, I shouldn't be afraid of the Fieldsboro Man-Baby because he is a holy miracle granted directly from Our Lord Jesus Christ to his mother, who prayed and prayed and did novenas and went to Mass every single day just so Our Lord would grant her a baby that would never grow up. Mother said they say that man-baby talks in a real deep voice like a movie star, and they say that anybody who's ever talked to the Fieldsboro Man-Baby can see he's as smart as the president. They say it's a shame, because if it wasn't for his mother's prayers keeping him little, man-baby could be somebody.

But my brothers told me that if I look in man-baby's eyes, even by mistake, or dare touch his beard, he'll turn me into the Fieldsboro Lady-Baby and I'll have to marry man-baby even if I don't want to. And his mother will sit me in the baby buggy right next to man-baby and push us both around town and show us off. My brothers said I'll be the new town curiosity.

I don't want to be a town curiosity! I don't know what to do! I don't know what to do!

My eyes start to cry. I sit down real fast and stack the mail as neat as I can on the steps right next to me. I try to untie my shoelace. But Mother tied it too tight. I can't undo the knot! I can't! I can't! *My hands are too slippery. My brain tells me, "Be slow, Patsy." But I can't. I can't. I tug and tug at my shoe. I tug until my shoe pops off and I flip backwards. My mouth starts crying because everybody can see my underpants. "Be slow, Patsy," my brain tells me. I bite the knot with my teeth. Then I poke my fingers in my shoe for Mother's paper, but when I pull it out, it's all crinkly and soggy.* I'm going to rip it! I don't know what to do! *"Iron it with your hands, Patsy," my brain says. I try. I try. But it's still crinkly.*

I pile the mail on my lap, but the claw lady gave me too much and it keeps falling off. I don't know what to do! I don't know what to do! *I stare at Mother's wrinkly note. I stare at all the envelopes.* I don't remember what to do! I don't know the letters! *Then I remember about the dot. I try to look through the dot but I can't. I try to match and trace. But my pointer finger is sweaty and keeps smearing the letters.* I can't see because my eyes are crying real hard. I can't stop. I'm going to make Mother so sad. I'm going to make Mother cry. I don't know what to do! *"Go slow, Patsy," my brain says.*

Then I see it! The letter C! C is my BEST *letter. C is Mother's letter.* C for Catherine. C for Catherine. *I wipe my nose on my sleeve.* C for Catherine. *I sing it. I keep singing it: C for Catherine. All the letters on the* C for Catherine *envelope match the letters on Mother's special note. I feel more better. I feel more better. I laugh. I laugh real hard. I laugh so hard my eyes start to cry again. I push the* C for Catherine *letter way, way down in my shoe. I'm so happy. I'm so happy. My toes sting like I'm stepping on prickles. I don't care. I don't know how to tie. I don't care. I don't care if I trip on my shoelaces. I skip all the way home. I skip and sing.* Put it in your shoe, Patsy dear, Patsy dear. Match the letters, Patsy dear, Patsy dear. Don't tell daddy, Patsy dear, Patsy dear. *When I run into the kitchen, Mother says, "Patsy dear, let me tie your shoe." She winks at me and I blink my eyes back at her and smile real pretty. Then Mother ties the laces real tight into a double knot. My shoe pinches my foot. My toes tingle. I don't whine. I am so happy.*

Daddy looks so silly sitting in his rocking chair with his glasses on top of his head. He snores like a lion. "Let's get you ready for bed," Mother whispers, and we tiptoe to my room. Mother sits down on my bed and pulls me on her lap. I can feel her smile when she pulls the letter out of my shoe. "You're a good little helper, Patsy dear — my favorite little helper." Mother says. She rubs my feet and my toes. I feel so good. I feel like a glowing star. I fall asleep staring up at the tinfoil stars twinkling on my blue ceiling. I am Mother's favorite. I am in heaven.

52

Pat

Mother told me she was going to Florida to live, that's all. I'll never forget it. I was sitting cross-legged on the floor in my bedroom cutting out paper dolls and Mother came in all dressed up in church clothes and the hat she only wore for Mass. My stomach started flip-flopping, because I knew it wasn't Sunday. Then she told me she was leaving and not coming back. And how I should be a very good girl and help Daddy. That's when I had a real conniption. Nobody could shut me up me when I had a fit. I guess that's why she took hold of me by the shoulders and said that if I would just settle down, she'd promise to me meet me at the post office in two days and take me to Florida with her.

Two days—that's all you have to wait, Patsy. Can you do that? But you have to keep it a secret. Can you keep a secret, Patsy? Mother will be very sad if you tell the secret. That's what she said. I remember those words exactly. Two days. That's all I had to wait. Just two days…

I can't stand to admit that I cried a lot over them two days, but I never said nothin' to nobody, not even Daddy. And I did like Mother told me. In two days I sneaked out of the house real early in the morning and waited on the post office steps for her to come get me. Mother never showed.

Brother Paul found me. It was getting dark. He said it was time to come home. I wouldn't go. I told him I was waiting for Mother. So he just picked me up and carried me. I screamed bloody murder the whole way. I kept kicking and punching him as hard as I could. When he finally set me down on the front porch, I raced to my bedroom and kicked the walls and kept kicking and kicking them. I kicked the walls until my feet were numb. I threw my dolls on the floor and stomped on their heads. I wanted to rip them tinfoil stars off the ceiling, but I couldn't reach. So I pulled my hair. I pulled my hair so hard, fistfuls came out. It felt good. I remember that—pulling out my hair by the fistfuls didn't hurt. It felt good.

53

Pat

How do I know if them letters in my shoe had anything to do with Mother leaving? It's none of my business. She came home, and that's it. No, I don't remember how long she was gone. How should I know? It was a long time ago. You're aggravating me, asking about this crap. All I remember is they brought her home on a stretcher. They wheeled her right into the front room. All I saw was a white sheet with brown hair sticking out. I was hiding in the corner. I thought she was dead. Are you satisfied now?

What happened? You're never happy until you get all the dirt, are you? I don't know what happened to Mother. Nobody told me nothin'. All I heard them say was that Catherine never did drive too good. They said she never even got to Florida. They said she hit a tree and the steering wheel got stuck in her stomach and they had to bring her back home. They said that's why she ended up with female cancer. They said the accident and the steering wheel getting stuck in her stomach caused it.

Why do I think Mother left in the first place? I don't think nothin' about it. I mind my own business. I don't know nothin' about people. Why the hell they do what they do. I don't ask questions. Why are you staring at me like that? Why do you say I look angry? *I'm not angry.* I'm not angry. I wish to hell you'd stop saying that. And stop looking at me like that. I'm not takin' any more of your shit. If I was angry, the only one I'd be angry at is you. Right now, I'd love to backhand you right across that smart mouth of yours. Then you'd see how smart you are. And I'm not crying. Damn it, I'm *not* crying. And don't you dare say I am. I AM NOT CRYING, DAMN IT. *I'm not crying.* You can go straight to Hell. I AM NOT CRYING.

54

Pat

I feel awful. I'm sick, I know I am. *If* I'm crying, *that's* why — *I'm sick* and old, and I can't help it — because I *don't* cry. I feel terrible awful. Nobody knows how terrible I feel. I don't have no good words to say how terrible. I feel as bad as when I was alive. I'm coming down with something. I got a headache. I'm sick to my stomach. I feel like I'm gonna die.

But my brain just reminded me that I'm already dead. Then how can I be sick? How can I feel like I'm gonna die when I'm already dead from being sick? My brain tells me that I been dead over a year now. I remember dying. I was in a bed with sides. In that nursing home. It was nighttime. Nobody was around. Just a bunch of other dying old ladies. I remember wheezing. My heart just gave out. I heard them say heart failure. But if my heart failed, why is it still beating so awful hard? Like it's gonna give out again?

A dead woman shouldn't feel this terrible. Dying was supposed to fix me. But it didn't. Dying just made me feel worse. Like every bad thing that ever happened to me got unstuck and it's back in my head again. All that crap is supposed to go away when you die; it's not supposed to get you again. It's making me sick. I'm having a heart attack. *I can feel it. I can't stand this.* I can't stand feeling this sick. If I had a razorblade, I'd cut my wrists right down to the bone to stop feeling this awful. Then you'd see how sick I am. I want to scream, *I wish I was dead.* But it don't do no good when you're already dead. And it don't make no sense to scream, *I wish I was alive.* Nothin's working. I'm sick. I'm old. Everything hurts. I feel awful and nobody will help me.

55

Pat

I made a fool of myself when I got old. My body started to go. I couldn't hold my water no more and I peed my pants. I cried over that—peeing my pants. I called myself a pig. When they told me I had to wear diapers, I wanted to crawl in a hole and die. I said I felt like a pig and started crying. I couldn't stop. I wish I could take back all that crying. I damn those tears to hell. You think I enjoyed crying in front of all them people? My kids? The doctors? Do you think I wanted to be a sniveling old woman? I hate sniveling old women. I never wanted nobody to ever see me cry. I'd do anything to force back tears. I'd rather bite off my nose to spite my face than let anybody see me cry. I'd rather smack somebody than cry.

They do things to you when you cry. They cut your heart out. They accuse you. They call you stupid. Ugly. Nuts. They turn away like you're a leper. They pat you on the head like you're a damn dog. I learned to hold my tears. I made them dry up. I didn't care if they set my eyeballs on fire. I wouldn't let them out. But then I got old and I couldn't stop them tears. It's no better now that I'm dead. I feel terrible awful.

56

Patsy

I never said this to nobody. I never even dared think about it. I don't know why I'm saying it now: it *hurt*. It hurt something terrible—Mother leaving me like that. My heart hurt like Jack Dempsey hauled off and punched it. When they wheeled Mother in the house on that stretcher, I was so happy to see her that I hid in the corner and cried my eyes out. They laid her in her bed and pulled the covers right up to her neck. I'd sneak in her room when nobody was looking just to stare at her. Her face looked as white as the sheet. She didn't open her eyes for a long time. I guess she was tired out from the accident.

Then one morning, she was standing at the stove stirring oatmeal, just like before. She looked the same. She wore the same housedress with no sleeves. Her hair still looked like a frizzy mop. But something was different. She was different. *I could feel it.* I put my arms around her waist and I couldn't feel her happiness no more. And I didn't know *why*.

I *knew* that Mother was different. But nobody would *say* she was different. Everybody acted like she was just the same. But I *knew* she was different—*I just knew it.* I couldn't make anything out, because she just looked like Mother. But she felt different. I *felt* it in my body. My nerves burned from her being different. Damn it, I don't have no good words to explain it.

I kicked things over Mother being different. I wailed. I refused to smile. Everybody called me cranky and miserable. *What's ailing you, Patsy?* they'd say. Every night, I cried myself to sleep praying to Jesus. I needed Him to tell me *why*. But He never did. Nobody said nothin' about Mother running away and being brought back. Not Daddy. Not brothers. They just acted normal. But it wasn't like the regular normal; it was different. It was like the air was holding back tears. It was like the walls had to cough but couldn't. The quiet was real loud. When people talked, they sounded different. What they said didn't match their eyes. And nobody ever told me *why*. I never knew *why*. I went crazy not ever knowing *why*. Fire ants. That's what it was—fire ants crawling all over me. Sometimes my whole body felt like it was on fire and nobody noticed. Nobody paid me any attention. Nobody told me nothin'. It's like I didn't exist. To this day, even being dead, I don't know why Mother left. I don't know what happened.

And now you're killing me with dumb questions that I don't have no answers for. You're making me bleed from thinking about all this hurt. I didn't have no idea that Mother's leaving hurt me. I never thought about my own heart, how it felt sore all the time. I threw fits because I was furious. I never figured I was sad. I guess I musta been awful sad. If I think about it, it stands to reason, don't it? Feeling sad? I never thought about that. Maybe I was sad.

57

Pat

It don't make no sense why I still got this dot…the telescope dot… from when I was Patsy. I don't know why, but I can look through it like I used to when I was tracing Mother's letters and see stuff real clear like. Stuff from before. From when I was Patsy. I hate looking through that dot. It's a sin to go snooping around and looking at things you're not supposed to. But I can't stop myself. I know I'm going to go to Hell for saying what I said about Sister Bobby. And about Mother leaving for Florida. And what I said about myself crying and everything. And telling about all that hurt I wasn't supposed to feel.

There's a lot you don't know. If I had a shot of vodka in me right now, I would tell you something that would make your head spin. Something I never told nobody about, not even Jack. Knowing you, though, you'll have me committed. You're like all the rest. I'm just dumb Pat to you. Good-for-nothin' Pat. I know you think I don't have nothin' useful to say. I *know* I should keep my mouth shut about this. I'm gonna hate myself if I tattle. But these damn thoughts are giving me a migraine. And I can't stand it no more. I'm goin' stark-raving mad. But if I tell you, you'll call me nuts. And I'll feel stupid. Then I'll want to die for saying it. But I *know* I'm already dead.

58

Pat

I don't know what dead wants from me. I'm confused. *Dying confused me.* I never felt loved when I was alive. How is it that I felt loved when I was dying? People were kind to me when I was dying. *They were kind to me.* They wrapped me in blankets. They rubbed me with lotion. My daughter looked me in my eyes and told me how beautiful I was. *I heard* Kathleen, and *it hurt.* It hurt my heart something awful to hear her call me beautiful. I started to cry. She dredged up all the ugly things I sewed up before I started calling myself *can't-do-it* Pat, and she called them *beautiful.* She used the word *artistic.* I'll never forget that: *artistic—me!* I never heard such a thing. She raved over my quilts, how I knew how to put all them colors together just right. And my hand-sewed dolls. And all those cross-stitched pillows I made. *Kathleen called me an artist.* She told me I have artistic abilities. She told me that if I'd had the opportunity, I could've been a real artist. Me—dumb, stupid, *can't-do-it* Pat—could've been an artist. *A real artist.* I started panicking and—what do you call it—hyperventilating. I couldn't catch my breath because I *saw* in her eyes and *I heard her.* I thought I was going to die from her kindness. I thought I was going to die from something deep down inside me that was crying harder than I was. Something dead that was choking on my tears.

I never made it past the tenth grade, so I'm not one of those snotty smart women. But if I was, I'd probably say that's why I'm brainstorming over whether to tell you about this thing I never told nobody about. Because of the kindness when I was dying. Because of how I felt warm. And cared for. And loved. Because of that remembering. I remember looking into Kathleen's eyes. I forgot about her love for me from before, from when she was little. But when I was dying, I *saw* it. It was there. I guess it was always there. I just forgot. Maybe I wanted to forget. I hate all that love stuff. I hate being soft. But when I was dying, I got soft. And something about it felt good. That don't mean that I'm soft now. It just means I'm remembering what it was like, letting in that softness. That's the only reason I'm cogitating on telling what I've never told. But if you cross me, I swear to God above, I'll give you a fat lip. I'll turn on you so fast that you won't know what hit you. And that'd be the end of you. You won't hear another word from me.

59

Pat

I'm watching you. I'm watching your eyes. I'm watching every move you dare make. If I see something I don't like, I'm gonna shut up. Mark my words. In my day, I cracked plenty of kids across the mouth—and an old lady, too. They all asked for it. If you're not careful, you'll be next.

Don't think I trust you. I don't. I don't trust nobody, not even myself. The only person I ever trusted was Jack, and look what he did—he went and died on me. There was one other person I trusted: my son Paul. He was a handsome dog, just like his father. Paul favored Jack right down to his smile. That's why I was soft on him. But he ended up cheating me out of my waterfront home in Florida with that baby-face smile. That's what I get for trusting.

I'm *not* soft on you. I don't trust you as far as I can throw you. Either you're up to something or you're a glutton for punishment. Why else would you be hanging around here itching for me to wail your tail? But for your information, I don't have nobody else to talk to and nothin' to do, and I can't stand this headache no more. So that's why I'm doing this. *Not* because I trust you.

I don't like to admit nothin', but all I can say is that people bein' kind to me when I was dying must be twisting my arm to act different. I'm gonna kick myself for saying this, but that kindness really meant something to me. It made me feel safe. I felt like Jack was holding me in his arms again. I'd forgotten about love…you know…how it feels. I never felt loved after Jack died. But when I was dying, I felt like I was loved again for a while. I guess that's why my heart got a little soft.

You know, I used to love to jitterbug. It made me feel good to dance. Everybody watched me. I was good at it, too. Brother Paul would flip me over his shoulders and then throw me between his legs—I could do it all. The more I danced, the better I felt. *Like I was somebody.* Like I counted.

That softness when I was dying made me feel like that—real good, real warm inside. It made me feel special. Like dancing did. Like how vodka goin' down my gullet used to warm the cockles of my heart. But that soft feeling I'm talking about wasn't from dancing or drinking.

That soft feeling came from words that—I don't know how to say it—made my heart cry or something. Them words Kathleen said reached inside me. Something like that. I don't have no good words to say it better. It's like my heart broke open and her nice words sneaked in and touched something I didn't know nothin' about—a bunch of words, *my old words*, buried inside me like chicken bones thrown in the garbage heap. I know you think I'm not wrapped too tight. That I'm a useless, crazy old woman with nothin' to say. Maybe *you're* the dumb one because you won't believe nothin' that didn't come from your own pinhead.

Now I feel like I'm gonna' have to cry, because I'm thinking I must be nuts—*you'll think I'm nuts*—because God's honest truth is that I got a real live picture of hacked-up words, *my hacked-up words*, in my head. Not like words lined up in a dictionary. But slaughtered words. Looking like the chickens Mother butchered.

Clear as the nose on your face, I saw in my head regular words that'd been ripped to shreds. Bashful words torn into bits. Ten-dollar words smashed to smithereens. Pieces of words I never had no right to say, dangling like bloody flags in mid-air. Somehow—and how the hell do I know how it happened?—them nice words Kathleen said to me were like some kind of magnet. Because they detected a bunch of gory, butchered letters crowded inside my head like useless junk and hooked them together. And them letters started to make words. It was like puzzle pieces comin' together. I *felt* it happening. I *felt* the letters sliding into place where they belonged. It felt like I was slipping a pair of old shoes on my tired dogs.

I felt real friendly toward them words. *I wanted to hug them.* I wanted to cry from seeing them all done up. It's not right to say that. That's stupid to think that I missed them. Who pines away for words she never had no right to? Only a crazy person pines for something so stupid like words. Don't tell nobody this, because it sounds nuts, but I feel like them words welcomed me home with open arms or something. Like they was glad to see me. *Me*—dumb, stupid Pat.

I don't understand. I know I always loved words. I could read them, but I couldn't ever use them right. I figured out that I was just thick-witted. But feeling the alphabet slide together like that into good words, words that made sense, words I could cogitate on, it was...I don't know... like someone turned a light on in the window for me. Oh, I'm gonna cry... seeing good words. Understanding them. Starting to think that maybe I wasn't retarded... It was like seeing Jack waiting on the steps to our house again and hearing him say, "I'm glad you're home, honey. The coffee's on."

60

Pat

I never even knew I carried around broken words inside my chest. I can't figure it out in my mind how kind words from the outside could find broken words on the inside and put them together again and organize them in my head. But now I'm scared that them words are worse than bad thoughts. I'm scared them words are gonna try to coax me to say too much.

Nobody understands how being dead has screwed everything up for me. I kept my mouth shut my whole life. I did what I was told. I never knew no different. I never had no good words inside me to say things. I never could *talk* like everybody else. I never knew how to. I was too dumb. This damn headache is getting worse. It's splitting my head in two.

61

Pat

For my whole life, I kept this secret. And now I'm scared I'm gonna' go to Hell for telling it. I been saying the rosary all night, praying that I'll keep my mouth shut. That I'll forget about saying anything. That my secret will just go away. But it won't go away. And my headache just keeps getting worse. My eyes are bleeding from this headache. I can feel the blood dripping off my face. I got nowhere to sit. Nothin' to drink to calm my nerves. No cigarettes. I got nothin' but a head full of bad words and *you*. I wish you would just kill me. Just kill me to keep me from talking. Because I can't trust myself because I can't stop myself. I need help. If you cared about me, you would kill me so I wouldn't talk. You could help me. You could kill me.

62

Pat

I got no more fight left. All my blood's gone. I don't care no more if you know my secret. It's about that telescope dot. I didn't only get it when Mother wanted me to learn her letters. *I always had it.* And I could look through that dot and see things.

You're looking at me like I got a screw loose. Don't you think I know only a lunatic can see things through a dot in her head? Weird things that nobody else sees? Magnified funhouse mirror bodies? Things crystal clear like they was projected on a movie screen across my brain? Don't you *surmise* that it scared the shit out of me? If anybody knew I could see what they couldn't see, don't you think they would've sent me to the bughouse and thrown away the key? I never told on account of that, but that didn't stop the *seeing.* That seeing dot was always there. All I had to do was look in it and it was like I could *see* the air. Like I could *see* "the blues" moping around on sunrays. Like I could *see* words light up, then get eaten alive by fire. Like I could *see* the wind. Not leaves and trash blowing *in* the wind; I could really *see* the wind—like I could see pimples on the ass of the wind. I don't have no better words than that to tell it.

I was titched, I musta been, because I could *feel* things, too. Things— invisible things—that weren't really things, but that I could still *feel.* I could *feel* people's feelings grate across my nerves until I wanted to scream. I could *feel* their voices crawling all over my skin, making me itch something terrible. I heard their words *loud* inside my head even when they said them quiet. Damn it, that's the best way I can say it. I could *see* noise in the quiet. When I was little, I could see under people's skin all the way down to their hearts. I could see their hearts breaking right through their eyes. I could feel hollering all bottled up, getting ready to explode. I could touch sadness—it hung off people's clothes. I saw things. I knew things. I *knew things I didn't want to know. I saw things I didn't want to see.*

Then I stopped. I couldn't do it no more. But the dot didn't go away. It was always there. I tried not to look, but I still saw weird things and felt them awful things, only I stopped paying attention. It was poison ivy, that damn dot. It still itched, but I stopped scratching. I think it made me crazy. And ornery.

I want to pull my hair out, because I don't want to go through all this shit again with that damn dot now that I'm dead. I don't want to *see* what I don't want to know. And I don't want to *say* what I see. My whole life I never said what I saw. And I saw a lot. Who am I to say what I saw? I got no right. It's not my business. Who listens to an old lady anyhow? They just ostracize you. Right now I'd like to ostracize *you*.

63

Pat

I wish to hell you'd stop looking at me like that. You're a real pisser. I don't like what I see in your eyes. I don't want to see it. I *hate* kindness. I told you that. The only reason I listened to Kathleen and got soft is because I was dying and didn't have no gumption left to fight.

Who are you, the devil? What do you want me to do, crack my skull open and let all the damn words spill out? So you can march me into Hell? You never lanced a boil, did you? You know what comes out of a boil? Pus. That's what those words are, pus. If I say them words, it'll be same as lancing a boil. Did you ever think of that?

But I don't have no choice no more, do I? You won't help me. And I can't take this headache no more. I can't even kill myself because I'm already dead, stuck here with all these words pounding inside my skull that don't have nowhere to go. I'm trapped in Purgatory, aren't I? That's what I'm coming to think. I'm in Purgatory. I'll be trapped here until I confess, won't I? I gotta come clean about all them bad thoughts, don't I? You coulda at least told me. Why did you just stand there and stare at me with that stupid look on your face? Why do I have to do everything myself around here? You coulda lifted a finger to help me, you know. You coulda said, "Pat, you're in Purgatory," and *told* me what I had to do to get rid of this splitting headache. Now I gotta iron all this out by myself. A lot of good you are...

64

Pat

I hate you for making me talk about myself. I don't got nothin' to say about myself that anybody wants to hear. Besides, what you say about yourself, they use against you. Mark my words about that. I *never* knew how to say things or do things right—not like other people. I was bashful. That's the only thing I can say. I was bashful. That's because I was ugly and dumb.

What do you think about this? In high school, they stuck me in the agriculture course and tried to make me a pig farmer. They wanted me to swap my pearls and seamed stockings for hog manure and bib overalls. It sounds funny. But there wasn't nothin' funny about it. How do you think that made me feel—that I was so stupid that the only thing I was good for was raising pigs? I don't have no good words to tell it right and that's making me real, real mad right now. The only word I can come up with is shame. SHAME! That's what I was, ashamed that I was so stupid and everybody knew it. That everybody knew I wasn't worth no more than slopping filthy hogs.

But I didn't say nothin'. I just stared them teachers down and sneered, "Suck my nose. I quit," and strut right out of that school, leaving them eggheads gawking at my backside. I gave them something to look at, too. I wiggled my rear end at their pointy heads and sashayed through them double doors like a real movie star.

I'm not going to say nothin' about crying over being so embarrassed. Over being no good for nothin' but stinkin' pigs.

All my life, I knew how ugly I was. "You're nothin' but ugly"—that's what Sister Bobby used to say to me. And that's what I saw every day when I looked in the mirror…ugly. "I hate you," I'd say to my ugly horse face. I hate everything about myself. Don't you think I wanted to be smart like Kathleen and everybody else? I tried to be funny, but whatever I said always sounded dumb. I saw how people looked at me. Like I was retarded or something. I knew they were rolling their eyes at each other—I'm not that thick. Every time I got up the nerve and said something I thought was funny or that I thought sounded kind of smart, I saw *that look*.

I hated myself for talking. I hated myself for living. I wished to God I coulda just laid down and died. I hated that everybody treated me like I was stupid. I hated that everybody treated me like I was wasting their time. I wanted to die to teach everybody a lesson. I wanted them to be sorry that I was gone. I wanted them to cry over me. I wanted to mean something to them. I wanted their respect.

65

Pat

Leave me alone. I'm in a terrible mood today. Terrible. It's because of the damn Delaware River. You got me thinking about too damn many things. And I been thinking about that damn river.

They threw me in the river. That's what they did to me. *They threw me in the river.*

66

Kathleen

They threw me in the river. They were just words that my mother uttered hundreds of times to me over my growing-up years and shook off with a shrug of her thin shoulders. Six pale, sterilized words. Weightless. Unattached to reality. Thought bubbles pulled out of the wind and lobbed my way. She could've been a blasé schoolgirl reciting a rehearsed line that bored her stiff. She'd just blurt out, *They threw me in the river,* then go on about her business dusting the furniture or stirring a pot of stew, leaving me hanging like a puppet on an invisible string.

What did my mother want from me? The kid who clung to her skirt so petrified of her collapsing and dying and leaving me stranded in a hostile, frozen world? Tears? Hysteria? A promise never to leave her? Admiration? Sympathy? I didn't know. But I felt frantic to, because I would've given her anything she asked for. Or at least tried to.

Mom, what happened? I'd ask. Then a vague complaint plucked from her long list of personal sufferings. *I haven't eaten a thing all day. I been working my fingers to the bone. I haven't had a minute to sit down.* Leaving me to fret that she was driving herself into her grave. Because those airy nonchalant words — *they threw me in the river* — weren't just words. They carried a secret message that wound itself around me in a leaden haze. They were harbingers echoing with menace, delivering a warrant for her death in the undertone. They were alarm bells. Blink an eye...snap a finger...step on a crack...and my mother would be gone! As if she never was. Those words foretold how she — not could be — but *would be* snatched away the second I turned my back. Those words kept me glued to her side, tangled up in her dark emotions even when I was apart from her. Without me, my mother would drown. Without my mother, I would drown.

I had to keep her alive.

67

Kathleen

My mother dealt in riddles: Sister Bobby, her scars, the river. Continually tossing foreboding hints at me like lit bombs to hold and lug about while she feigned innocence. Sinister clues alluding to a variety of horrifying incidents that she refused to clarify. Behaving as if my concern were excessive, ridiculous. As if taking drowning—or rape, or beatings, or suicide attempts—seriously was stupid. And weird. The look in her eyes always flat, distant, empty. Acting as if what she said meant nothing. *Nothing.* When all along darkness loomed, overwhelming me with muffled death threats that my mother kept flinging my way as if she were tossing me candy.

So I stood affixed to her side, a carved statue. Silent. Protecting. Assuring myself that she was alright. That she was breathing, at least for now. *They threw me in the river.* She offered no explanation. Attached no story. There was no tale of freezing water. No protest of cruelty. No declaration of anger. No admittance of terror. No indictment of *they* as guilty. No mention even of who *they* were. I reacted to this undercurrent of menace with anxious, stoic vigilance. I *had* to take away her pain, but I couldn't *see* it—I could only sense it. And it was immense. Bottomless. A place of loss. Churning quicksand capable of swallowing her body whole. Her unvoiced pain was bloat in the air I breathed. Melding myself to her was the only way I knew to ward off her troubles. At least I could try, because I *had* to do all I could to keep her safe so I would be safe.

I became an attending appendage offering friendship, comfort. Finding ways to slip beneath her bad humor and into her heart. Massaging her moods. Finessing her out of her brooding gloom. I commiserated with her; made her laugh; put the bright in her eyes. And I, her adoring admirer, would be richly rewarded. A happy face. Impulsive outbursts of exciting energy. *Brainstorms,* she called them. *Why don't you take off from school today and we'll rearrange your bedroom? How about we sit down at the kitchen table together and pick out some nice stuff for you from the Green Stamp catalog? I have an idea...let's go buy some Tastykakes.*

Forget heaven, angels, and harp music. I had it. Right there. Me and my mom. It was the drug I couldn't get enough of. The elusive high I chased. I was after the swoon. The intoxication of connection with her. I appointed myself faithful sidekick—Tonto to her Lone Ranger—obsessed with willing away her unhappiness using the powers of my own grit. I became her guard dog, watching always, instantly ready to pounce at the whiff of a threat. By protecting my mother—by absorbing her endless litany of angry complaints, by turning away from my own petrified heart and investing in hers, by being an obedient confidant who never argued, never griped—I protected myself from the grief of her drowning in the river. And there was always a river looming.

68

Pat

If Kathleen's trying to get me to say I'm sorry, she's barking up the wrong tree. I don't go in for apologizing. I don't accept no apologies either. Don't come crying to me with *I'm sorry.* My line is, *If you're sorry, you wouldn't do it.* I'm not apologizing for nothin'. You're not gonna get me to apologize. Kathleen's not gonna get me to apologize. I didn't do nothin'.

69

Pat

I don't know nothin' about nothin', I told you that. Kathleen was just my shadow. She followed me everywhere. She was tied to my apron strings, that's all. How do I know why? That's just how Kathleen was. She didn't cry or pester. She was just my shadow. I guess I got used to her. I must have. I never yelled at her to go away.

I *believe* I told you I'm not one for looking back, so I don't know why you keep bothering me. I *told* you I don't go in for that stuff. If you *force* me, I guess I'd be *forced* to say that I liked having Kathleen around me. I remember sometimes feeling real soft toward her. That's when I'd open my big mouth, I guess, when I felt soft toward her.

If you *force* me to think about it, I'd be *forced* to say that Kathleen *listened* to me. That's all, I guess. She didn't talk back. She paid attention. Jack wasn't like that. Jack *did* things for me. He was always making jokes. He liked to make me laugh. He always wanted me to be happy. But Kathleen. I don't know…she took everything I said serious. She didn't go in for jokes.

Do I remember telling her things? What things? I didn't tell nobody nothin'. If you *force* me to say—all I did was drop hints. You can't put nobody in jail for that. After I dropped a hint, I'd clam up. You couldn't pry my jaw open. If you wanted to know more, it was up to you to figure it out. You aren't going to get me to say that I'm terrible for dropping hints. That's nothin' but a bunch of crap. Everybody dropped hints. Everybody acted like they didn't say nothin'. Everybody did. Not just me.

Who's everybody? What do you mean, *Who's everybody?* Everybody I knew, that's who. Just everybody. Everybody in my family.

I'm getting ready to blow a gasket. I can't think no more about Kathleen. Or about dropping hints. If I dropped a hint, it was up to her to figure it out. I blame Kathleen for listening to me anyway. It was her own fault. I didn't do nothin'. She shouldn'ta listened to me., She was always hanging around me, wanting me to talk. It was all her fault.

70

Pat

I haven't slept one wink. Not one. I can't rest with all this crap going on in my head. You don't know what it's like bein' this dog tired. The dot's been following me everywhere. Every time I close my eyes, there's that damn dot. Bigger than it ever was. That dot's got a hold of me. I can't make it go away. I guess because I'm so worn out. Now I'm afraid to say what happened with that dot. Because I think I might be half off my rocker. I didn't know you could be dead *and* crazy.

When I was alive, they always called me ornery, a real pistol, stubborn as a mule. I acted miserable. I made people miserable. Ask anybody. I threw fits. I'd bite off my nose to spite my face. That's what I was famous for— bitin' off my nose to spite my face. Or I'd shut up and never speak a word. *Nobody* could hold a candle to my grudges. Don't you think I knew that I was carrying on? But once I got goin', I couldn't stop it. I *wanted* to carry on. But now, things are getting different for me. I'm learning some things around here. Due to that dot I was always so afraid of. That's what I'm thinkin'.

Listen to what I'm tellin' you: I didn't want nothin' to do with that dot, but it wouldn't go away. So last night, I started hollering at myself about how I better chase that thing out of my head pronto. I shook my fists and cussed up a storm. *Damn it, Pat,* I shouted, *get that damn thing out of your brain right now.* If I'd had a pair of scissors handy, I woulda cut every last strand of hair off my head just to show how fightin' mad I was. I hollered at my mind to shut up. *I'm sick of you,* I kept hollering. I was so pissed off at myself. For being stupid. For being a dumb woman. I hollered until I couldn't holler no more and I had to sit down before I collapsed. I couldn't tell where I was. It didn't look familiar; everything around here is strange. I just sat down on the ground and closed my eyes.

I *never* admit to being tired, but here I am admitting that I was too pooped to pop—a stupid old woman, too tired to open my own eyes. I always hated women who griped about being tired. In my day, I *never* griped about being tired. Sitting there with my eyes closed, I started cogitating on how I used to gripe about a lot of things. But *never* about bein' tired. Who wants a tired old hag around? But then I started thinkin', maybe I *did* gripe about being a *little* tired a couple of times. *Maybe.* I don't remember.

Did I really *say* that I was dog tired? That I was too pooped to pop? I did, didn't I? That's a kick in the teeth to me. Because I remember warning myself *not* to say those things to you. I told myself, *If you say how tired you are, Pat, you're gonna have to pay for it.* But after that, I went and said it anyhow, didn't I?

I hate weak women. Now I'm one of them. What is being dead doing to me? Not in a million years, not if my life depended on it would I ever—*ever!*—confess *the truth* about how tired I was feeling in my other life. They take away everything you have if you show them you're feeble. Do you know what old women have to *pay* for bein' old? Don't tell me you don't know what I'm talking about, because I'll beg to differ with you.

I hate like hell sayin' this. I hate like hell sayin' that I was so tired that I almost fell down flat on my face. That's a disgrace—being that tired that your legs go. Plus, it's not right havin' to see things you don't want to see because you're too tired to run away. But I didn't have no choice, because that dot was stuck right there in front of my eyes I couldn't open. I wasn't asleep, either, because I'd just sat down. And I wasn't dreaming, because I still felt myself. I felt how it was *to be* myself. But *what* was my feeling? Lookin' into that dot, I asked myself over and over, *What is this sensation drivin' me to drink?* I wanted an answer, because I felt like I weighed a hundred tons.

Then a word rose up in my brain big as the sun: *SAD.* I was dumbfounded from being kicked in the teeth again. *Sad.* I never thought much about feelin' sad. I never believed in it. But sitting there collapsed like an old bag, that's when it dawned on me. *I been sad.* All this time, ever since I been me, I been sad. I just sat there, feeling sad, too tired to fight.

71

Pat

I was never a big woman when I was alive, but I felt like I carried a lot of weight. I used to check myself in the mirror all the time to make sure I wasn't fat. I could see how ugly I was, but I knew I wasn't fat—not like them stout ladies. I took care of my figure, ask anybody. Why did I feel so fat when I only weighed 120 pounds? Somehow looking into that dot, I found out. And it's weird. I saw that I *was* heavyset. But not on the outside where fat ladies carry their weight, all in their guts and backsides. I carried all my weight on the inside. In my heart. I was heavyset *inside*, where nobody could see.

I never heard anything about bein' heavyset in your heart. Staring at that dot, I started to get the drift—what it's like to feel sad. You know chapters in a book, how they have headings? So that you know what the chapter's about? That's like what I saw. The word SAD, in capital letters like it was a title. I got kind of scared and thought if I could only get my legs to work, I'd run like a bat out of hell. But I was shaking and my legs were poor, so I just took a deep breath like I was dragging on a Raleigh and blew it out to calm my nerves. That's when I started feeling different. Strange. Soft, I guess. Like the worry leaked out and left something soft. Some kind of softness around where my heart is.

Then I started to think about bein' sad. How I never knew the word for what I was feeling. I never had the word *sad*. That don't even make sense, not havin' a word. But I didn't. I swear to God, I didn't. I knew about sad clowns. Red Skelton. Emmett Kelly, the sad hobo. But I never knew *I* was sad. I never knew I was a *sad woman*. I don't have no good words to tell about that. I always thought I was just a miserable person. I didn't know nothin' about bein' sad. I remember lookin' at that dot and thinkin', *Is this what sad feels like?*

I feel like I should call myself crazy as a loon. Holler at myself that

I'm off my rocker. But I don't have the mind to. I hope to God you don't say I got a screw loose. I don't want to be a crazy old woman no more. I can't do nothin' about bein' dead, but I don't want to be crazy.

72

Pat

You're gonna call me nuts. I know you. I know that's what you're thinkin'. That I'm just another nutty old woman with a vivid imagination. But I swear on Jack's grave that I have butterflies from that soft thing puffing around my heart. I keep telling myself, *Pat, you have no business gettin' butterflies like you're a teenager pining over Frank Sinatra.* I can't explain none of it. I feel like my heart is swelling. Or melting. Or breaking. I don't like this. I'm afraid. This sensation...this soft sensation...it's all over me. Like an afghan. I'm scared stiff. I'm too scared to move. *I need air.* Why am I just sitting here like a dunce? I don't even know where I am. My stomach's flip-flopping. I feel like I'm ridin' a rollercoaster down the shore. Or Frank Sinatra's just asked me to dance.

I have to think about this. Maybe it's just my nerves getting to my heart, giving me a heart attack. I always had bad nerves. My nerves always gave me headaches. Not a day went by I didn't have a headache. Maybe all this is just my imagination. Maybe I'm dreaming. I got to figure this out. If I don't, I'll never get another minute's peace. I have to concentrate. I just need to concentrate.

I remember when I was in school. I wasn't any genius with arithmetic. I never could add like they taught. But I figured out my own way. It wasn't nothin' to write home about, but I could come up with the right answer. When Jack and I used to bowl, everybody asked me to keep score, because they knew I could add right. That made me feel good bein' asked to do something like that, something important. Running every single pin, every spare, every strike through my head like I did made me feel smart. I would total each frame by fives, then go back and add or subtract the leftovers with my fingers and tally it all up and come up with the score. I remember concentrating like I was lookin' through a...through a... Like I was looking through... a... dot...

I'm sick to my stomach. I got to sit down. *But I'm already sitting down.* I can't even hear myself think. All this time, that dot I thought I got rid of was still there, wasn't it? That dot I didn't want to have nothin' to do with. All along, I was still lookin' through that dot. I can't understand this. I want to, but I can't. I don't have no thoughts to understand it. How can I understand somethin' when I don't have nothin' to look at? How can I explain to myself what the dot is when I *don't know* what it is? When I can only *feel* it? When I can only *feel* my eyes getting smaller and smaller and what I'm lookin' at gettin' clearer and clearer? Like watching the point on a pencil get sharper and sharper.

This crap's givin' me a terrible headache. I can't stand it no more. You don't *know* what it's like to be an old dead woman. I don't know nothin' about all this stuff. Nobody told me. Nobody told me nothin' about any of this crap. You don't *know* what it's like thinkin' you know what there is to know. Thinkin' that what you know in your head is set in cement. I didn't know nothin' different except what was in my head. Now I feel like I don't know nothin'. *Nothin'.* I don't know whether I'm comin' or goin'. I can't keep goin' through this. I can't put two and two together no more. It's not like tryin' to figure out how to add up numbers right.

73

Pat

It takes me a long time to calm down. That's just me. I always been that way. You gotta understand, I don't know nothin' about all this. I always thought I was so stupid. But I been cogitating. I been tryin' to be real nice to myself. I deserve it after all this.

I been thinkin' about that whole dot situation. Tryin' to figure out how it works. I'm picturing the dot like some kind of circle that I can look into. That's the best way I have to describe it to myself. And how lookin' into that circle thing, I'm starting to see things about myself I never knew. I'm seein' that I made things happen when I concentrated. I don't understand how that can be true. How *I* made things happen when I concentrated on them. Like adding numbers up right. But that's what I'm seeing. How I *did* learn things. That I taught myself things. I wouldn't call somebody stupid who could add up numbers right. It stands to reason, don't it? *Oh, my nerves. My nerves.* I never thought about me, Pat—dumb, stupid Pat—doin' things that took a brain. I never dreamed it.

74

Pat

My heart's throbbing real fast on account of that soft feeling. If it don't stop, it's gonna burst. My heart's gonna burst from something I didn't know could be true. It's gonna burst from something I never felt before. *It's gonna burst from feeling smart.* That don't make sense. How can I burst from feeling smart when I felt stupid my whole life? How can my heart feel smart? How can seein' how I added up numbers count toward feeling smart? But I would call my kids smart if they got an A on an arithmetic test, wouldn't I?

75

Pat

When I was alive—when I was young raising my family—nobody, *nobody* kept a better house than me. You could eat off my floors. I was proud of that. I had a strict routine: wash sheets on Monday, dust and vacuum good on Tuesday, scrub floors and bathrooms on Wednesday, iron and bake on Thursday, quick dust and vacuum on Friday so everything would be nice and clean for the weekend. That's how I got things to be just so. I liked to straighten up. I always been like that since I was a kid. I can't stand things messy.

I don't know why, but my brother and son were hoarders. I couldn't stand the junk they had all over the place. Can you believe my son stored a load of greasy, dirty car parts *in his front room* when I was living there? And you wouldn't believe the stacks of papers on the kitchen chairs... *I couldn't stand it.*

That's how I felt about the soft thing—those soft feelings—all balled up with my nerves. A big pile of junk I couldn't stand. It was drivin' me crazy tryin' to straighten it all out in my mind. Tryin' to look at things—at how I felt, I guess you would say—a little bit at a time. I got these deep feelings but I never thought about them. I never said nothin' about my feelings. I never tried to figure out things like that. I never had words for my deep feelings. I never sorted them out like I did the dirty clothes when I was getting ready to do wash. Those feelings were just a big blob stuck on my heart, no different than the stinkin' garbage stacked in my son's front room.

I want to scream right now telling you about this—it's makin' me so mad again. So pissed off. *Why am I mad?* For the simple fact that there I was sittin' like a damn dunce, a real dum-dum because I couldn't iron nothin' out. Because I tried to open my mouth to scream at the top of my lungs from bein' so aggravated over bein' so empty-headed, but nothin' came out. Nothin' but a squeak. Like a mouse. I tried to kick myself in the ass. I kept shouting in my mind, *Get the hell away from all this shit, Pat.* But my whole body was watery. It wouldn't get up. It wouldn't move.

I called out to Jesus. *Help me! Help me!* Why couldn't somebody help me? *Pray to Jesus, pray to Jesus*—that's what they always told me to do, *pray to Jesus* when I needed something. But Jesus wasn't nowhere to be found. There wasn't nobody. I was all alone. And my brain wouldn't figure, it wouldn't figure. I said the hell with this shit. I'm not doin' this. I don't need to put up with this shit.

Then the thought came to me: *Pat, maybe it's not a thing you can figure out.* And my mind went blank. I took a long drag, wishing to God I had a real cigarette, and let the air out real slow. I kept doing that, pretending I was smoking. Remembering how I used to love to smoke. How I always loved the sound of crinkling cellophane when I opened a pack of Raleighs. That first whiff of tobacco. Thinkin' about touching the cigarette, it was so smooth. The smell of sulfur when I lit the match. I loved how the first drag burned my throat.

Thinkin' about how it was for me smoking let my nerves start to calm down, and I started to feel soft and warm. Real soft and warm. Like takin' a bath, only I wasn't wet. I used to like to take baths, you know. That was a long time ago. I forgot how it felt to take a bath. It felt good.

I didn't take to feeling good when I was alive. It never lasted. Not once did feeling good last. But sitting there with my eyes closed, feeling soft and warm, I didn't worry no more about the good feeling goin' away. I just let myself feel it. It was like when I was sunbathing down to Sunnybrae Beach when my kids were little. They had a lifeguard down there, so I didn't have to worry. I remember just closing my eyes and everything fading away, everything but the sun. It was so warm on my shoulders. On my face. I forgot about that, too. Sunbathing. Why didn't I do more of it? It felt so good. Oh, I wish I hadn't forgot all about taking baths and sunbathing when I was alive.

But I'm not alive! *It's all gone now.* Every damn one of my chances is gone. I want to smash my fists through a window, I'm so pissed off about that. If I could, I'd crack you across the mouth so hard your back teeth would rattle. Because you're askin' for it. Because you're makin' me think things I don't want to think about. Because you think you know everything. And you don't. You don't see nothin' but what you want to see. You think you know me? You've never seen me throw a *real* conniption. I've scared off better people than you. If I could have a shit fit right now, I would. And you'd be runnin' away with your tail between your legs. *You don't know what I'd give... You don't know what I'd give...* And I wouldn't give a shit if they sent me straight to Hell, either. You don't know me. I'm famous for bitin' off my nose to spite my face. You don't know one damn thing. Not one damn thing.

There's no reason on God's green earth why *I* have to be the one to explain myself to myself. *I don't have no words.* Aren't you listening to me? I don't have no words. Are you stupid? Don't you understand English? Can't you hear me? *I don't have no words.* You should be explaining *me* to *me*. Why do I have to go through all this crap to understand what's in my own mind? When I thought I already knew?

I'm not puttin' up with this shit.

76

Pat

You should know by now it takes me a long time to calm down after I get all riled up. That's just me. I don't even remember what I said to you. When I get upset, I just start griping. And I can't stop. I always been like that.

If it makes you feel any better, when I got calmed down, I kept askin' myself, *Pat, what the hell's wrong with you? Why can't you just listen?* Then I asked myself, *Listen to what? Listen to what?* YOURSELF! YOURSELF! That's all I heard: YOURSELF! But it didn't seem like it came from my mind. It didn't come from outside either. It came from...I don't know where...a feeling, or something. It came from...

I'm trying to catch it. *Oh, I have it! I have it!* I have to say it fast before I lose it. The word YOURSELF!—an echo! That's what it was! An echo...a nudge...against my heart—came from the same place from when I used to make homemade cakes and I *knew* how much vanilla to add without measuring. I just felt it. I just knew it. It was just in my fingers. And how my fingers felt on the bottle, and knew how to tip it just right so I'd get the right amount of vanilla. The precise amount. *Oh, I see.* It's like salt. Like adding salt to beef stew. How I never measured! *I just knew!* I knew the right amount. Not too much, so it wasn't salty. Just enough so if you wanted to add more salt, you could. My fingers, my hands just knew. They knew what to do! That echo in my heart... It's like a "feeling sound" that tells me.

I have to say this fast, before I start gettin' riled all over again and wreck everything. Before I feel too ashamed to say it. Too ashamed of myself for wanting something so bad. Don't you think I want all this stuff to be true? The dot? The soft feeling around my heart? With God as my witness, I could cry, because *I want it all to be true.* But I'm afraid it's not. I can feel myself startin' to get mad again, because I'm afraid that somebody's gonna take it away from me. Somebody's gonna ruin what I'm starting to see. I'm afraid you're gonna tell me everything's all a lie. That I just made up that dot and the soft feeling. It's nothin' but my stupid imagination. You're gonna make me look like a fool. A damn stupid fool for believing what I'm starting to believe. *For believing myself.* You're gonna go and take all this away from me.

Now I can't stop crying. *I love that soft feeling.* I love it so much it hurts. I hate myself for sayin' that out loud. I never wanted nobody to know about how much love I kept hidden away. Now that soft feeling is bringing all that stuff to the surface, makin' me feel good again. And it's gonna go away like everything else I ever wanted did. I know it will.

That soft feeling is love, isn't it?

77

Pat

What if that's what made me ornery? *Love.* Things I loved bein' taken away from me. Mother. Jack. My home. And it sounds awful weird, but what about my words, too? What if it's just like Kathleen said? What if my words were really taken away from me? What if Bobby really did beat my words out of me?

Oh, good grief. It's startin' to make sense. I always loved words. I don't go in for makin' a fuss over things, but I loved words as much as anything. But I could never get them to do what I wanted them to do. They'd never come out right. Nobody heard what I was tryin' to say. Everybody just ignored me. Everybody, except Jack, made me feel like I didn't count for nothin'. And I'd get so mad, I'd feel crazy and I'd just get ornery. And I know that's how I acted. I didn't know what else to do besides throw fits. People paid attention to me when I threw fits. But then I got to be an old lady and nobody paid attention to my fits no more. When I had a conniption, they just acted like I had a screw loose. Or they just ignored me like I was invisible. And I'd be embarrassed. Nobody saw me. No matter what I did, nobody saw me. So I just shut up and started sleeping a lot. I was dead before I died.

I don't know what's gonna become of me. I'm tired of throwin' conniptions. Even though my brain is half tellin' me that all this stuff is horseshit. The dot. The soft thing. Feeling warm. My brain is tryin' to get me to act ornery like I always did—like I always do. But I don't want to keep gettin' fired up no more. But my mind wants me to. My mind keeps tellin' me that what I'm feeling isn't real. But somethin' about what my mind's tellin' me don't feel right. Somethin's tellin' me that all this stuff *is real.* And I'm thinkin' that to think different feels like I'm giving something real nice the brush-off. For my whole life, I brushed off nice things. Nice things hurt my heart real bad. But now with that dot and the soft feeling, I'm starting to see something else.

Now you got me thinkin' about mud. How grimy and gritty it feels, like cold, dirty dishwater. How if you don't scrub your hands good, all that slop dries out and cracks your skin open. Leavin' your hands feeling tight and crusty, rough as sandpaper. And you get cranky because dry skin feels a lot like splinters sticking you. I'm starting to think about that. About mud. About my heart feelin' muddy. About how mud makes your skin feel stiff. And I'm wonderin' if maybe I get ornery because of that dried-up mud feeling in my chest makin' my heart feel like it has dirt on it. And I try to make that awful heavy feeling go away by bein' ornery and throwing conniptions.

I'm thinkin' something right now. I'm thinkin', what if that heavy dried-up mud feeling is really sadness? But how can feeling sad feel like heavy, dried-up mud? I always thought sad was what you felt when you went to funerals. Or how I cried over Rhett Butler leaving Scarlet O'Hara in *Gone With the Wind*. Or when Jack died. Those were sad times. I felt my heart crying. Like it had real tears. But now I'm wonderin' if there's another kind of sad that I didn't know nothin' about. Not sad where I'm cryin' all the time. But sad that feels like heavy slop stuck in my heart.

I told you about Mother; I know I did. About after her bein' brought back from runnin' away. How when I hugged her, she looked the same, but she *felt* different. Heavyhearted, I guess you'd say. I remember that. I remember throwin' fits because I couldn't get rid of that heavy feeling I got from her. That heavy feeling went straight into my own heart. I didn't cry. I had fits. I guess Mother was sad. I never figured that.

I'm startin' to understand. It feels like I'm learnin' how to read. When before, the letters didn't make no sense jumbled all together like Scrabble pieces. Then all of a sudden, I could make something out of the Scrabble letters. I started to *see* words. Words that made sense. That's what I'm tryin' to say about sad. I'm learnin' a lot about being sad that I didn't have no idea about. I'm learnin' to *see* sadness. I'm learnin' about my sadness bein' real. And how I didn't know it. How my heart felt like slop due to bein' sad. I can hardly believe it. I can hardly believe I know this. I never trusted myself to know nothin'. I think they call it an inferiority complex. I read about that a long time ago in one of the books I got from the library. I never knew I had a complex. I just thought I was just me.

Oh, good grief! A word just came to me! A word I never went in for: *depression*. I always thought that word was just a bunch of malarkey. I'd hear somebody say the word *depression* and think, *What the hell do you have to be depressed about?* They were just complainers, that's what I thought. Too lazy to get up off their asses and do something. What the hell's depression? It's nothin'. That's what I thought. That thought was set in cement in my mind. That was the end of it. Anybody who said about being depressed aggravated me. I wanted to slap their hangdog faces. *Depressed.* Get up off your fat ass, that's what I thought. I still think that way. I *hate* depressed people, layin' around in bed all the time. Cryin' at the drop of a hat... Hypochondriacs. That's what they are. Mopin' around all the time. Who do they think they are? God's gift?

78

Pat

I don't know why I'm startin' to cry again. Something made me think about Mother. I see her in bed with that white sheet pulled all the way up so I can hardly make out her face. She's cryin', just laying there cryin'. I see me beggin' her to get up. I see my face lookin' down at Mother. I'm cryin'. I'm cryin' somethin' awful.

I don't know what to do about this. I feel terrible. I feel terrible for…for…this probably isn't right to say…I feel terrible for that little girl. That little girl, Patsy, with the banana curls and the big bow tied in her hair. I'm watching that little girl tap dance. She's so happy. She's laughing. She wants to make everybody smile. I see her crying. Crying so bad she can't stop. I wish I could make her stop. But I can't.

She's crying and crying now on account of Mother leaving her to go live in Florida. She's chasing Mother down the street. I see her chasing that old black Chevy. Her skinny legs are running and running. She's holding a doll. Real tight. Against her heart. She can't wave her arms because of the doll. She doesn't want to drop her doll. She runs and runs. All the way down to the end of the street. Down to the corner, crying every step. She cries watching Mother's car drive away. She can't see that car no more. Now she's screaming. She's screaming for Mother to come back. She's screaming bloody murder.

I am screaming and screaming. *I* am trying to get Mother to hear me. Trying to get Mother to come back. She doesn't hear me. She don't come back.

It was *me* all along. *It was me.* Not some made-up, make-believe little girl runnin' down the street. *It happened to me.* I never even thought about it that way. Mother leavin' and me chasin' after her like that with my doll and my broken heart.

79

Pat

Mother's being wheeled into the front room. I see her right now through the dot. It's happening right in front of my eyes. She's on a stretcher. There she is. *I see her.* She's all broken and quiet under the blanket. I feel my heart. It's bursting with joy! Joy! Joy! Just to see Mother again! Just to see Mother come home!

Oh no. There's something else. I feel my heart squeeze. It's squeezing on account of her pain. *I feel Mother's pain.* I *feel* the pain in Mother's heart. It hurts. It hurts. I'm in her bedroom. It's dark. She looks like a lump under the covers. I am kneeling beside her bed, crying. Watching over her. I am trying to keep her safe by reciting the rosary. I'm rolling the beads in my fingers—they're smooth and cold. I am full of perfect prayers for the Blessed Mother. I implore the Blessed Mother to make Mother get up. I beg her to implore her son, Jesus, too. *Please, please let Mother get up.*

I hear Patsy begging Mother to get up. *But it's me.* It's *me* begging, "Mother, get up. Get up. Please, get up." It's my very same heart. *My very same crying heart.* It's *Pat's* heart breaking. It's *Pat's* eyes crying. It's me. *This all happened to me.*

I am lost. I am lost.

80

Patsy

She's laying in bed under the covers, Mother is. Nobody saw me sneak in here. It's dark. Daddy pulled down the shades on account of Mother not gettin' a headache. I try to hold Mother's hand. It's limp. Like my ragdoll's. I stand so still, looking down at Mother. I whisper, "Get up, Mother. Get up." I can't stop myself, I start to cry. I'm crying because Mother won't move. I don't hear Daddy come in. He says in a real sad voice, "Go play, Patsy, Mother needs to rest." But I won't move. He takes my hand and tries to pull me away. I yell, NO! so loud that Daddy jumps and warns me that if I don't pipe down, I'm gonna wake the dead. I hear Brother Paul's footsteps. "Shush, Patsy," he says. But I won't shush. I keep crying louder and louder. I work myself into a fit. Brother picks me up. I kick. I scream. He carries me away from Mother. I wish I could give Brother Paul a black eye.

81

Pat

Mother was different when she finally got up out of bed. Nobody would say she was different. But lookin' through that dot, I see now that she *really was* different. I see that it wasn't me bein' stupid. Or bad. Or ornery. That dot is showing me that Mother wasn't *Mother* no more. That dot's showing me that Mother was like a cracked egg. That dot's tellin' me that they brought Mother back to the house after the accident but *Mother* didn't come with them. That dot's showin' and tellin' me things. That dot's showin' me that I was *right*. That I wasn't just angry little Patsy havin' conniptions. *I was right.*

Oh good grief, I was right.

I was right.

Mother was different. I *knew* it—I *felt it* in my heart. I *felt it* in how my heart hurt. I *felt it* in the "different" Mother's words. The "different" Mother talked different. The "different" Mother started talking about dying. I *heard* her. I heard it in the words she said and the words she didn't say. I saw dying in her eyes. They looked different. They weren't round no more. That's the best way I can tell it. Her eyes were slow, like she had to drag them to look at something. She didn't have no more dance in her eyes. And nobody paid attention. *But I did.* I paid attention. I tried to ask about the "different" Mother. But they all said it was my imagination. They said to stop bein' a pest. *But I was right.* All along I was right. *I was right. I was right.* I can't hardly believe *I was right.*

I'm not accustomed to bein' right. I'm accustomed to everybody else bein' right. But all along *I* was right. With God as my witness, I never knew that. I never knew I could be *right.* I never knew I could be right about something so important. I swear on my own grave, I didn't know I was entitled to be right about anything.

82

Pat

I'm startin' to see. *I'm startin' to see.* I can't explain it right. But my heart feels light, like I'm part of the sun. Or floating on the sun. Or floating on sunlight. I don't have no good words to tell it. All I can say is, my spirits are lifting. I feel like when I was going up the elevator in the Empire State Building when I was a little girl. Like a balloon soaring up. Something like that. That's the best I can explain it.

My chest feels empty. Not bad empty, or lonesome empty. Light empty. Like the mud—all that grimy, gritty slop stuck in my heart—is melting away. Draino. That's what comes to mind. I used to pour Draino down the kitchen sink to unclog it. I haven't thought about Draino since before Jack died. When I was a housewife. Draino, that's a dumb thing to think about.

I'm daydreaming about bein' on that little beach in Sunnybrae Village. Back in '50s. Hearin' the kids playing in the background and feeling the sun. When I close my eyes, I can see the sun light up my eyelids. I'm remembering something I forgot all about. I remember that soft thing. I remember it bein' around my heart then, too. I forgot all about that. I remember now…feeling so contented…laying there in the sun…the kids safe and me just relaxing, getting a tan.

I can't believe I had the soft feeling before and I forgot all about it. I can't believe it's back.

83

Pat

Oh my nerves. It's comin' together for me now. I just got a word for Mother. I gotta think quick. I don't want to lose it. I got the word: *DEPRESSION.* That's the word! That's the word! *Depression!* That's the word! It fits! Oh my good grief in heaven. I got the *word*.

I remember now. I *see* it. *I see it all.* I see the "different" Mother walking around with her slow eyes. I see Nanny and Jesse comin' to live. I see me havin' a conniption on account of havin' to leave my bedroom with the stars on the ceiling and move upstairs into that twat Bobby's room. I see the "different" Mother filling up the house with brats and stinkin' diapers. *I see Mother forgetting about me.*

Not for the life of me do I want to say anything bad about Mother. I feel sick to my stomach over this. I'd rather cut out my heart than speak ill of Mother. She never slapped me, not once in my whole life. She wasn't ever mean to me. But looking through that dot, I'm seein' things different…about Mother. And me, Patsy, the little girl. *And me, Pat.* About my heart—my same heart from when I was little to when I got old. It's the same heart I got now. That's what I'm seein'.

Mother forgot I was alive. I don't think that was fair. I never said that in my whole life, that Mother forgot about me. And about how that wasn't fair. I can't understand why I'm sayin' this now. Why I'm thinkin' this. It's just comin' out of me like air. It's ringin' like a bell inside my heart. It feels like a slot machine goin' off. How it pounds your heart with excitement. Then rains out all those quarters.

I gotta say it again so I can hear it better. *Mother lost me. Then she forgot about me.* She forgot that she lost me. She didn't see me no more. I wasn't there. *But I was there.* But I *felt* like I wasn't. I was lost. I can't describe it, but I lost myself. I evaporated. Mother didn't see me, so I couldn't see myself. I couldn't see myself in Mother's slow eyes no more.

I couldn't see *Mother* in Mother's eyes no more. She wasn't there no more. That made my heart hurt something awful. It still hurts. It still hurts. When I was an old lady, I dreamed about Mother. I cried for Mother in those dreams. I begged her for help. But she didn't hear me. She didn't listen to me.

I have a word now. I feel like I won the lottery. I didn't have nothin' before. Not one thing to explain about Mother. I didn't know there was anything to explain. I thought, what's done is done. Mother leavin' don't mean nothin'. It's over. It's in the past. Seems like a hundred years ago. I guess it is almost a hundred years ago. That's a long time. That's an awful long time for a heart to hurt.

But now I have a word: *depression*! You don't know what it's like to have a good word to use, a word I can use for Mother. You don't know how much it explains. I don't know how one word can explain so much. How one word can just knit together my heart from bein' broken. I can't figure it out. It don't make sense to me. But it paints a picture, that depression word does. It helps me know things. It helps me know that Mother *was* different after the accident. It helps me know that I wasn't crazy. Or ornery. It helps me to know that I was feelin' her heart. And her heart bled into mine. And I couldn't stand for feelin' so much pain. Hers and mine. It was true. *It was all true.* I never knew about that. I just thought I was cantankerous. And crazy. But it was *me* feelin' Mother's hurt. Then I hurt. It's all true. I wasn't crazy. I wasn't crazy after all. I have a word now. I have a word I didn't cotton to before: *depression.* That turned the lights on for me.

Something's growing inside that dot, inside me. It's like my heart is warm dirt for the thing to grow. I'm starting to feel something. I'm starting to feel it grow. What I didn't know before. And what I've forgotten. I'm starting to feel my heart grow warm. I'm letting my heart stay warm. I want to see more so I can understand. I want to look into that dot. I want to look into the sun and learn what I don't know. *I want to understand.*

84

Kathleen

I am watching her, we all are—my father, my four brothers, and I. We've gathered here at the lake's edge to witness a miracle. To attend a triumph of major proportions, at least in our family. I suppose that in the holy world, it would count as a baptism. In our world, it's bigger than that. This is nothing as simple as a miracle. This is my mother slaying the devil with her own two hands. All summer long, she's been taking swimming lessons, determined to conquer her terror of water, determined to allow her face to get wet. Determined to swim.

My mother does not take kindly to getting her face wet. Taking a shower is an ordeal. Not only because her face might get wet but because she could drown. Right there. In the family bathroom. Drowned by a showerhead while the rest of us are watching Milton Berle. The idea of stepping out from under the trickling stream of water to save herself is as farfetched as her rowing a boat across the Atlantic Ocean. My mother does not approve of any body of water. That, of course, includes the ocean. Her bathing suits are cute, strapless numbers chosen for the art of tanning, which is what my mother does when we go to the shore. She smokes, passes out peanut butter and jelly sandwiches, and tans. She never gets wet, though once I think her big toe accidentally touched the foamy residue of a wave.

All that has changed this summer. My mother has been taking swimming lessons. *She's learned how to swim.* That's what she has been telling us. Now, we are a group of six excited fans assembled on wet sand to observe a spectacle of Olympic proportions, anxious to cheer the triumph of her accomplishment. All she has to do to pass her swimming test and become a real and true swimmer is jump in the water and breaststroke over to the lopsided raft where kamikaze kids launch themselves, trying to drown each other with cannonballs. It's not a ten-mile swim, but it might as well be.

I am staring at her with such intensity that I can hear or see nothing else but the rush and gasp of her panicked breathing and her heart knocking hard and loud against her ribs, trying to flee her chest. From where I am braced at the lake's edge, I can barely make out her facial features, even when I squint and shade my eyes from the sun with both hands. I don't have to see or hear the detailed intimacies of her physical fear; I am actually experiencing her terror as if it lives somewhere inside me.

The diving board where my mother stands rests at the end of a long wooden dock that stretches far out into Gropps Lake and hovers over water that is at least ten feet deep. Nobody calls it Gropps Lake down here. This is Sunnybrae, a private lake for paying residents of Sunnybrae Village *only*—those families who manage to scrape together the twenty-five bucks to join for the season. The houses may be new and tended to, but money doesn't flow freely in Sunnybrae Village. Not a Cadillac or mink stole in sight. Station wagons and dungarees rule in these parts. The only "rich" man in the neighborhood turns out to be an embezzler.

In the Allen house, money *never* makes an appearance. My father keeps his cash locked in his wallet, his wallet glued inside his pants pocket, and his pants pocket nailed shut. Scare up the nerve to ask him for a dime and he explodes like you're trying to steal the last few remaining hairs on top of his head that he keeps sculpted and lacquered into a fixed, undulating wave. Dare beg him to join the beach club? You'll find yourself spending the summer with a wash bucket and a list of chores that will teach that smart mouth of yours a lesson. *Think you're unhappy now? After scrubbing floors on your hands and knees every day, you'll learn what unhappy is. You better change that miserable attitude of yours around here if you know what's good for you.* That's my father: tightfisted; hardheaded; angry. Except toward my mother, who is his one and only soft spot. Only she could melt him enough to get him to cough up the dues for this extravagance of summer pleasure. No lowly, ungrateful kid would stand a chance.

So thanks to my mom, here we are, full-fledged members of the Sunnybrae Village Beach Club with proper badges and all. As official badge holders, we believe that our lake is sparkling clean even though it is located at the far-end point of Gropps Lake, which everybody knows is famous for the poop that bobbles along its currents in gooey piles. Members of the Sunnybrae Village Beach Club blame the poop on the people across the lake who squat in ramshackle bungalows and flush their toilets right into the water and whose grimy kids pee in the lake which, of course, no kid from the pristine, glistening side of the lake whose parents fork over dues for swimming privileges would ever do. Luckily, the poop from across the lake does not spoil our side of the lake. So, the raw sewage drifting past our tidy beach—which had *nothing* to do with the epidemic of Sunnybrae Village kids contracting impetigo—is merely a curiosity. As trivial as a sideshow attraction at the State Fair. And a minor inconvenience on sweltering days when the turds won't cooperate and insist on taking their lazy time to float out of sight, keeping all of us paying members dripping in sweat and jeering at the lifeguard who holds our summer fun in suspension, since he alone can give the all-clear signal.

This morning, though, everything shouts GO! Sunny sky. Scorching heat. No poop. My mother secured in swimsuit and bathing cap. In position on the diving board. The lifeguard hovering close by. Our eyes glued on her. *GO, MOM, GO!*

My mother is not going anywhere. Least of all in the water. She looks sculpted. A block of granite hacked into the form of a petrified woman. Bolted to the plank a foot or so from the edge. She is not budging. I can tell by the way he is leaning into her and patting her shoulder that the lifeguard—what is he? Sixteen? Seventeen?—is coaxing her. Whatever he is saying—*Come on, Mrs. Allen. You can do it. You want to pass your swimming lessons, don't you? All you have to do is jump off the diving board—* is not working. I pull my brain into a tight knot of willful thoughts and fire them at her like arrows sheathed in heroic courage. *You can do it, Mom,* I plead over and over to myself as if my thoughts can will her into success. But she is as rigid as the board she is fused to. Frozen. Unmoving.

It happens so fast that I don't know if she was pushed or if she jumped. All I see is a statue toppling into the lake. A fleeting shadow arcing against the sun. A quiet splash. Unearthly silence. Except for my heart plundering all the blood and oxygen from my eleven-year-old body. Hours. Maybe only seconds. The lifeguard. Leaps. Muted thrashing. Great echoes of panicked lake water churning in a funnel of muffled sound. No screams. No shouts. Just thrashing. And rapid, clumsy spurts of jerky motions. The noisy comings and goings of ordinary life around me vanish and plunge into a single tunnel of sound—water slapping water and the husky vocal grunts of effort.

My mother flailing. The lifeguard, one arm slung across her shoulders, dragging her through the murky water. My mother flailing. The lifeguard dragging. Flailing and dragging. Flailing and dragging. Water sloshing in slow-motion geysers. Garbled, thick moans stolen from a nightmare. Then my mother. Clawing at the wooden ladder. The lifeguard. Both hands on her behind. Pushing, pushing, pushing. Pushing her up onto the dock. Her legs, as wobbly as a baby's, collapse beneath her.

She looks dead.

85

Pat

They threw me in the river.

86

Kathleen

I've never given much thought to that day at Sunnybrae Lake. But from the span of years, the connection seems now so glaringly obvious. My mother's eerily detached lament about being tossed into the river viewed alongside her raw animal terror in the lake. She was eight years old again on that summer morning on the dock. Rushed backward in time to a little girl. To Patsy. Grabbed by the waist without warning. Hurled overboard into the frigid, pitch-dark water of the Delaware River. The shock. The panic.

Always I've wanted to dismiss my mother's erratic, disorderly conduct as stubborn misbehavior, invented for attention seeking, for garnering sympathy. Generated just to annoy the hell out of me. The exhaustion of her acting out—of her rebellion against the air she breathed; her hostility toward compassion—overwhelmed and humiliated me. I never understood why my mother couldn't be the poised, articulate mother in public that she was with me in private. I never understood why she broadcasted her gaping emotional wounds to the world over the loudest public address system she could find.

87

Pat

I dunno…

88

Kathleen

Many times over, I have said that I am a storyteller in a family of secret keepers. For as long as I can remember, I have bristled at the sensations of intense, prickly forbidden truths escaping, thorn by thorn, from behind immense, oxygen-sucking barricades of vapid double-talk erected by family members. Or slipping through the cracks of their sewn-tight lips like poison spores. These pent-up masses of walled-off truths razzed me with insistent energy. Potent with electricity, what-was-never-to-be-spoken-of radiated through layers of hoarded silence like laser beams, buzzing my skin, leaving ghost nettles to burrow deep into my bones, fueling powerful episodes of the heebie-jeebies. That made me want to screech or run. Or do both.

I could feel *phony* strangling on its own message, and it made me crazy. Time and again, the invisible force of the forbidden-to-be-spoken-of hit me like an energy bomb of amassed, unspoken words minus the letters, clamoring and vibrating as it clashed with lip service, idiotic buffoonery, and maddening riddles dead-ending in the pitch-black tunnels of funhouses. Those bombs were like racehorses pulsating with exertion, straining at the gate—their stink and sweat loosed even with their power bridled. Those invisible secret truths hauled electric tonnage and tormented me, a bashful girl, as an actual presence pushing and thrusting, demanding recognition.

There was little choice except to deny, deny, deny the fidgeting of smoldering contradictions huffing and puffing beneath benign chatter. Strain not to notice buried truths shuddering across the airwaves like bad music. Struggle to disregard the sensation of it scraping across my thin skin with the sharpened tines of invisible forks as the heebie-jeebies blistered my nerves and zinged me with such intensity that it pinched the oxygen right out of the air I needed to breathe. *Keep quiet,* I commanded myself.

Because the heebie-jeebies offered no excuse for disrespect, petulance, failure to smile brightly, or any disobedience of the absolute, final voice of authority: my omnipresent father, who was "the premier truth knower of all truths" since he simply took it upon himself to decide what was true in *all* matters of all life, including past, present and future. Including *my* past, present and future.

I didn't know I was as dumb as a doornail until "the premier truth knower of all truths" informed me, mocking me for my stupidity. Assuring me that I was permanently disqualified for anything requiring a brain. Ridiculing any whisper of intellectual scholarship. And nixing all uppity notions of higher education, since according to "the premier truth knower of all truths," he wouldn't waste the time or one red penny on me because as *the* premier truth knower, he *knew* where I was headed. Apparently where I was headed required no snooty education: *Hello, shitty toilets and snotty noses.* But I digress.

So there I was, trying not to dash around like a crazy girl swatting imaginary cooties, definitely a major violation of the code of affability and good manners that was strictly enforced by *the* premier truth knower. *I can't stand it, I can't,* I argued with myself. I knew that punishment for violating the code of my father's absolutes was far worse than any torment doled out by invisible what-was-never-to-be-spoken-of grandstanding for an audience of one. What I *had* to do was escape. But to where? How could I outrun my skin?

So, what's a bashful girl inflicted with invisible ants-dancing-on-her-skin to do? What else? Ignore the beestings of hidden truth. Or at least try to. Battle to dismiss its ominous presence. Fight to reject the evidence of contradiction clearly visible in the stench hovering in certain eyeballs and flattening the glisten like a cold iron in a lead hand, or pressing down on stoic shoulders like dense smog, breaking delicate wings unseen by the naked eye. Batter myself with blame as if from the dirt of my warped imagination, I produced those electrical charges and the X-ray vision that was supposed to belong only to Superman. Condition myself to believe anyone, *anyone* but myself. And trust those who were bigger, stronger, louder, and older than me. Acknowledge *them*—the fakers, the phonies, the bullshit artists, the pigheaded double-talkers—as *the* truth knowers and kowtow to their *gifted* demagoguery.

And disbelieve myself. *Always* disbelieve myself. *Always disbelieve myself.* And accept as gospel what farted out of *anyone else's* mouth despite how it fouled the air with stink. Even when the truth knowers informed me that I was dimwitted. And that I was NOT FUNNY, which came as a surprise since I'd always had a funny bone and didn't realize that it was something to be ashamed of until the truth knowers told me. I didn't know that I was an embarrassment. An affront to all humanity. And that sooner or later I would get what was coming to me for daring to crack a joke or laugh at something that WAS NOT FUNNY.

The message from *the* truth knowers came across loud and clear: I was flaky, miserably inept, offensive, permanently unqualified, and hopelessly naïve due to pipedreams and notions of magic carpets, which I blame on Walt Disney.

Then I grew up.

89

Kathleen

The more I grew, the more other women rendered null and void began sprouting up right before my opening eyes. Obedient string puppets—women rigged to *the* truth knowers with thick, dark ropes I could sense but couldn't see. Women whose skin *was not* bruised black and blue from beatings. Women whose limbs were not broken from blunt force trauma. But women whose spirits—*whose genius*—lay battered and numbed, deadened beneath the weight of the truth knowers and the wet blankets they carried around like righteous cargo: tirades, sermons, criticisms, punishing silences, smug barriers, and the occasional compliment that came by way of a left hand.

I started noticing then that the women around me did not rank up there with the truth knowers. They were relegated to the sidelines. Refused opinions and viewpoints. Deprived of decision making, even on personal matters. Whatever unique talents they possessed, or might develop, rendered useless. Entangled in the strings of puppetry. Unsung and barely visible. Every aptitude suppressed. There were artists, writers, poets, intellectuals, mystics, anthropologists, scientists, designers, craftswomen, culinary masters, storytellers, sensitives. Women forced out of their destinies and into a world of obedience where no tolerance existed for even a suggestion of their true brilliance. A world from which there was no escape. Except by way of illness and incapacity.

As I matured, I noticed how they folded into themselves, bone by weary bone. Women I loved. Never uttering a word on their own behalf. Passively surrendering to *the* truth knowers who leaped out of the underbrush like vampire trolls. Young women. Middle-aged women. Old women. *My mother.* Complying. Treated by *the* truth knowers like trainable, too-big-for-their-britches children. I saw women *handled*. Dealt with. Exploited. Ridiculed. Demoralized. Condescended to. Shut down.

Often in ways so subtle that the only indication of injury was a brief flinch in her eyes when *the* truth knower slammed her heart. The obedient string puppets—the women I loved. *My mother*—never rebelled. *Never.* Not openly. Not outwardly. Not honestly. And that both disgusted and terrified me, because the ropes that strangled them snaked toward me.

When I think of those women, I think of misery. A climate of tight, serious, personal woe. Reoccurring train wrecks. One calamity after another—tragedies, misfortunes, discomforts. The knocks never letting up. I don't remember when I first sensed that *something* was up with their never-ending, hobbling crises. But at some point, *something* puzzling—*something* contradictory—began settling over me like an itch without a rash. *Something significant* I could not identify. An uncomfortable awareness that *something* didn't exactly fit. Didn't feel right. Something off kilter. Something that looked like one thing but hinted at another. A vague suspicion of a back door. Of a secret passageway no one else was wise to, carefully guarded by a fire-breathing, guilt-slinging creature capable of incinerating all doubts and slaying all doubters. And that fire-breathing guilt-slinger did not hesitate to hammer the hell out of me, accusing me of casting aspersions, fault-finding, and backbiting for my mounting notion that the visible woe of an obedient string puppet was *not* the real problem. That the woe was only the *spokeswoman* for what rattled beneath. It wasn't enough that those thoughts horrified me with guilt; they parked themselves permanently across my shoulders in a weighted, sodden mess.

Still that nagging perception that there was *something* else, something elusive wouldn't leave me. Yet it evaded capture. Refusing to be defined with words. Drifting about me like a haze. Only to evaporate when I tried to study it. Though if I'd given one thought to the powerful force of a single, measly weed pushing itself up through concrete, I could have easily figured it all out and *voilà!*, the muddled, conflicting pieces of the puzzle of the obedient string puppets and their woes would have fallen neatly into place. But I didn't understand then the ways and force of nature, the determination of the inner fire to fight for its survival.

Had I understood, I would have noticed genius finding a way.

Marveled at the ability of a broken spirit to express its outrage by commandeering a physical body with the battle cry, "Move over, sister—I'm taking charge here." Organizing revolts. Staging mutinies. Rallying around an obedient string puppet and her damaged thought system to meticulously cover all tracks of her fight to fly. Employing maladies, afflictions, infections, depressions, crippling obsessions, and handy diversions for leaks of wild, helpless anger.

I couldn't understand it then, the swell of underground spirit-rage—that potent, unseen force of feminine inertia—forging its way. "Magically" creating conditions and circumstances. Foolproof excuses. Rock-solid justifications. Formidable, proof-positive evidence. *Everything* and *anything* required to grant an obedient string puppet permission to *steal* what already belonged to her, but what she was *not* entitled to: oxygen and a place to breathe it; bits of personal time so her brain might solidify. An obedient string puppet battling a migraine was "forgiven" for needing isolation. And QUIET! And a break from duties of the flesh.

Without the aid of "magic," obedient string puppets would be labeled thieves—trespassers on their own bodies, which they knew they had no actual claim to. Ill health was the "magic" ticket that could rescue them. Ill health dangled offers of respite and allowances for the strictly forbidden directly in front of their faces. Ill health was the pass that permitted them to *steal* back body parts exhausted from being used and handled by anybody with an urge. No lectures. No condemnation. *Peace at last.* That monster—guilty conscience—kicked to the curb. At least temporarily. How easily surgical butchery of a deteriorating uterus conveniently bypassed the "sin" of birth control. *It wasn't her fault.* The *surgery* made her sterile. Made having more kids impossible. Anyone—even the parish priest—could see it wasn't her fault. *If it was up to her...if her body hadn't failed her...*

I *saw* them. I *felt* them. They haunted me. They still do. Hungry, obese women. Women behind closed doors, crying in pain. Decaying from cancers. Suffocating, wheezing. Hitting the booze stashed in closets and dresser drawers. Sullen, obstinate women seething with venomous, hidden rage, slicing scapegoats to pieces without ever flashing a blade or batting an eye. Women slumped in chairs—relieved of all duties—too sick, too drained, too sad to move. I listened to them whine. Watched their eyes sparkle as they recited their lurid tales of ghastly diseases and debilitating frailties in such vivid, melodramatic detail, their performances deserved a theater.

Beneath their ramblings, though, immersed in the shadows, I heard the screeching of their secrets layered atop the hoard of family secrets squalling for a break. And all this fanatical energy made me insane. Insane! *What was it?* I *needed* to know. Whatever was concealed raged like blistering sunburn on pale skin. Hummed like a swarm of agitated bees inside my skull. I may as well have been a chicken dashing and darting around, blindly groping, crying out for its severed head.

I had no words for what I *knew*. No way to communicate the scattered, broken pieces of fragile women clawing inside my bones and scraping glass shards across my nerves. I didn't know how to verbalize then that the severed head *had* to be reconnected with its body. That the lonely heart *had* to be reconnected with its yearning soul. That the genius spirit *had* to be connected to its restrained power, to its abandoned voice. In some way I cannot begin to explain, I *knew* that the fugitive ghosts—the living, intangible, dynamic energies of what was refused voice—were frantic to unify themselves. To be made whole. To become, at last, complete.

Apparently I was the only one. No one else in the family, including my mother, seemed the least bit bothered by a hoard of untold stories screaming for attention by masquerading as a swarm of invisible, feverish bees buzzing and stinging unsuspecting bystanders. It's not like I didn't ask for the stories. What's the old adage: "Ask and you shall receive"? I asked. I pleaded. I *received*, all right—silence, blank stares, scary warnings of communist takeovers, stonewalling; slight of hand, shaming, and the worn-out, "You ask too many questions, Kathleen."

So I gave up. But not really. I just shackled the questions that rushed and surged inside me. And when I slipped—when I embarrassed myself in front of *the* truth knowers by showing too much interest in the past, too much sincerity in my quest to learn—I absorbed the shame of rejection, the humiliation of ridicule, and the disgrace of my ignorance that fled to my cheeks in a riot of red. I learned to blunt my curiosity and swallow my observations for terror of being caught under a shit storm of mockery. I trained myself to be silent. Even as the heebie-jeebies howled at me. And stabbed my innards.

Still, I *couldn't* give up. The ghosts were relentless and drove me nuts with what I could feel but couldn't see. I don't think my mother knew what to do with me. I'd complain and complain to her, *Mom, why don't I have a loopy aunt hiding out in a root cellar? An old lady rolling around in her bed, rambling on about aliens contacting her through her false teeth?*

I *needed* a loony bin relative! Someone alive! Someone animated! A handful-of-a-woman who would talk! A conjuring, Viking kind of woman. A crazy old crone leading the charge into worlds oblivious to the blank-staring, obedient string puppets. A mischief-making kinwoman who would understand the beckon and press of vivid peculiarities bumping about in a shy girl's head. An *honest* woman full of truth and tales. A living witch who would appreciate the headwind of chaotic images and dismantled words crying to be expressed, crash-landing inside a little girl, only to remain stalled like neglected pleas. A kindred spirit who would understand that I was trapped in a cookie-cutter split-level scrubbed clean of poetry and spirit but still bustling with its ghosts.

Okay, no loony bin aunt. How about a willful slave who escaped evils and pointed to her scars and revealed their stories? A withered woman proud of her disobedience. So bold that her courage defied the constraints of time and reached down and anointed her descendants, including girls—including me—with power and belief in themselves. And bestowed her mysticism—a legacy of chants and oils and Voodoo spells—upon a shy, offbeat girl. *Nothing.* If such a woman existed in our family, she'd been banished from memory long ago.

What does an obedient, white-bread girl endowed with the stirrings of the mystic do? Beg. *"Mom, tell me something."* *"You ask too many questions, Kathleen."* And off she'd go to dust or vacuum.

The brush-off didn't work. I still pined away for relatives with admirable—or at least eccentric—pedigrees who did not exist; who never existed. Or who did exist but whose antics were banished away with piercing glances that scared the obedient string puppets silent. And reduced lives lived to clandestine whispers, eventually erasing them forever from conscious recall.

How many times do I have to say that I felt them—the tired ghosts, the energetic ghosts—both the living and the dead. They stared out at me from the shadows cast by my family tree. Expressionless. Thin cardboard cutouts. Varnished with whitewash. Or they danced in the shadows, fleshed with vitality, refusing to be still. They were all there. They all wanted to speak. They all wanted to be seen. Maybe they thought I could be their intermediary. Maybe it takes a ghost to know a ghost.

So I pestered and pestered my mother to tell me tales of our relatives. Finally she caved. Finally she gave me *something*. My mother gave me George Washington.

90

Kathleen

George Washington is family. Of course this connection is not plotted on any dull genealogy chart stretching back to the times of powdered wigs and men's ponytails prettified with striking black bows. Nor does my link to George Washington have anything to do with dusty history books, cherry trees, tedious lectures on his fine character, or his role as our nation's first president. No, my kinship with George is much more personal. It involves turf and storytelling that played my heart like a schmaltzy violin with weeping strings—how awful that George was forced to have all his rotted teeth yanked out with pliers and swapped for wooden ones with splinters. Though come to find out, the wooden teeth story is a myth. Seems I wasted a lot of good sympathy on a situation that was no more than exaggerated yarn spinning.

Rotten teeth aside, to understand my link to George Washington, you would have to understand how a particular type of territory ownership works—the "I *live* there so it's *mine*" kind of attitude. This is an emotional thing, a possessive thing. It fits in the same category of sporting a tee shirt with the name of *your* city or *your* favorite football team splashed across your chest in pink neon. It's *personal*.

My roots with George are *personal*, going all the way back to Bowman's Tower—an impressive, once-working fieldstone monument that to this day still stands tall on a rise across the Delaware River over there in Pennsy. And where the General himself is rumored to have kept watch for the Hessians during the Revolutionary War. Truth is, back in the day I pretty much owned Bowman's Tower. This is due to the fact that my parents would drag the five of us kids for fun weekend outings of stumbling up its spiraled, rickety stairs without falling over the railings. Imagine...I trudged up the very same steps hundreds of times that *George Washington* himself did, and peered out—hands shading my eyes in lieu of a telescope—over the *same* bucolic landscape. All without plummeting to my death. That more than qualified me to assume ownership of the tower and claim a personal relationship with George, who did not meet his death by tumbling over the wall either.

Lest you think that Bowman's Tower was my only close—and pitiful—connection to George, it was not. In fact, George Washington was very big in Trenton, New Jersey, which also happened to belong to me. This is because my father was an important man with an important state job, and his office was smack-dab in the center of the most important city in New Jersey whose streets George himself once roamed, or at least rode through on his noble stallion. So, do you see how beautifully all this worked for me and George Washington? How violins and home turf set the tone? And all this before my mother actually nudged him out of the pages of the encyclopedia and gifted him to me in real life.

My mother *didn't* tell stories. My mother *complained*. Why George Washington was different, why she chose him for her first and only venture into storytelling, I don't know. It's not like she was political, or had an interest in history, or even a concern about other people's lives—least of all dead presidents. But that was my mom—a guarded woman trailing a sack of unsolved mysteries behind her. So it was that one day my mother simply pulled George Washington out of the thin blue air and slid him into a story. A story that she would repeat to me over and over, whispering it with such solemn, muted reverence in such gentle, soft tones that I felt as if she were entrusting me with a cherished memory for safekeeping.

With details so vivid, so mesmerizing, so deeply touching, I latched onto that story as if it were legitimately recorded in calligraphy somewhere in the hidden, meager annals of our family pride. As if George Washington truly were a forgotten ancestor erased from history like all the others who passed through the Evans clan—my mother's people—only to have their hearts disregarded and their lives dismissed. It felt clandestine, this story of my mother's about George Washington, a secret resurrection of an outcast from exile. And daring. An act of quiet defiance that risked a swift and stern penalty should her betrayal be discovered. Her family's commandment of deaf-muteness hung in the air like wet dirt, and the recounting of anyone's history seemed cause for punishment under their law of absolute silence and apathy. Maybe because the telling of *anyone's* history might leave a path of breadcrumbs leading directly back to *their* history and all family history was OFF LIMITS.

Despite the consequences looming in the clouds, my mother—this one time—enabled herself to step into the sunlight of storytelling. Outwardly this looked unremarkable, humdrum, white-bread boring—what mother doesn't tell her kid stories? And nothing like the event of mammoth proportions it epitomized—a *colossal* departure from her family's rigid tradition of keeping your mouth shut about all things at all costs. Lucky guy, that George Washington. And lucky me—evidently, George didn't pose that much of a threat to any unsightly family secrets. All my pestering had finally paid off.

Actually, as I think of it now, nearly sixty years past, the story is not really *about* George Washington, though I have always remembered it so. *George Washington* is simply the title, the place where the enchantment begins, the home my heart returns to in memory. Odd that it never registered with me that the George Washington story was more about *the occasion*, the experience, about the warmth of my mother weaving a tale. How I felt cuddled by her opened heart. The ecstasy of being invited into her confidence. The buoyancy of my emotional starvation satiated by her undivided attention and the comforting sensation of her intelligence. Add to that bliss a *spellbinder*—exactly my kind of story—*told by my mother.* My mother actually sharing a story with me, allowing serious words and thoughtful images to creep out from beneath the wall erected by her complaints. It was utter enchantment. There was my mother, bringing George Washington—a safe, harmless ghost—to life through a tale of exquisite misery and extraordinary bravery. In those brief, sporadic moments, I glimpsed my mother connecting to her lost self. The woman I longed to know.

It would be a mistake to imagine the George Washington story as a sit-and-listen-wrapped-in-a-quilt-sipping-hot-cocoa kind of thing. My mother didn't sit and chitchat, much less snuggle. My mother stood and kept busy. Not to say that she didn't ever perch on the edge of a chair when the occasion called for it, just that she spent most of her time on her feet, giving credence to her daily gripe at suppertime, *This is the first time I sat down today.* No surprise, then, that George Washington made his initial appearance in our tight, humid kitchen while my mother was *slavin' over a hot stove,* as she would call it, wedged between the wall and her fated destiny, stirring and stirring bubbling rice pudding made from scratch, ferociously circling the wooden spoon lest the milk scorch and the rice stick to the bottom of the pot and *ruin the whole damn thing.* This would be a major calamity and could easily deteriorate into a string of muffled curses and threats to sling the entire mess at the wall.

Which mother stood at the stove—worn-to-a-frazzle mom, fed-up mom, or sort-of-happy mom—depended on her patience and the mutual cooperation of three essentials: the concoction of wet and dry ingredients, the assortment of cooking gear enlisted for the task, and the fickle gas flame. If what she was beating the tar out of with her wooden spoon didn't aggravate her and was boiling along nicely and not congealing into hideous, gelatinous lumps, chances are that the sort-of-happy mom was the one standing at the stove. That's whose side I was glued to when George Washington tumbled out of history and into our kitchen: the sort-of-happy mom. There I was, breathing her air, staring at the churning milk, speckles of perspiration forming on my upper lip, when she started to *talk.* Maybe the sultry heat in the kitchen or the repetitive Zen motion of the spoon lulled my mother into a sense of peacefulness and safety so alien to a woman who never let her guard down. But she began weaving a tale that I embellished with my own hunger.

In hushed tones set to the scraping of wood against aluminum, my mother wove the grinding saga of General George Washington's exhausted, tattered militia slugging through blizzards and sleeting ice. Through the magic of her words, I saw bare, frozen feet wrapped in filthy rags. A trail of bloody footprints staining the driven snow. And these images settled in me like a forever wish. Enveloped in the waft of scalding milk and vanilla extract, wrapped in poetic imagery, I fantasized this to be a real and true family tale of grit and honor. The General with his fancy uniform and champion warhorse and manly accomplishments was the star of the story. But the real prize, the real daydream I pocketed as a treasure, was not about George Washington but about his magnificent soldiers trudging around barefooted in a raging, blinding snowstorm. I was so swept up, so captivated by the personal, dramatic agony of a ragtag band of skeletons leaving bloody footprints in the new-fallen snow, that right then and there I fired George as my territorial kin and conjured up a militiaman to replace him as the long-forgotten, magnificent ancestor of mine: *Uncle Magnificent*.

Uncle Magnificent glides into my mother's story without assistance from her words. He emerges from a plume of a gentle, swirling snowfall as a boy trudging ten miles uphill to school on an empty stomach wearing cardboard shoes. Or maybe ragged leather shoes stuffed with cardboard, or yellowed newspaper, to keep the snow from soaking his woolen stockings. Sometimes he does not even wear shoes or stockings at all. His frozen, bleeding feet make him heroic. When General Washington calls, Uncle Magnificent answers. He does not need boots.

There is no Uncle Magnificent. George Washington is no kind of kin. But my mother—*my mother*— braved a story and *told it*. And that does truly live as a sit-and-listen-wrapped-in-a-quilt-sipping-hot-cocoa kind of memory.

91

Pat

I got reasons for things—I'm startin' to see that now. I'm startin' to really see that my heart hurt more than I can say. That heart hurt never went away. Not for my whole life. I see that now. My whole life I lived with something inside my chest that felt damp and heavy. All I can say is it sat inside me like some kind of lump. Like my heart felt like a hump on a camel's back sittin' in the center of my chest. I can't explain it right. An old dowager's hump in my chest instead of a heart, that's what it felt like. And it ached somethin' terrible. My heart always felt weighed down with anchors. I always felt like I was ready to drown. That's the best I can explain it.

I just said *drown*, didn't I? I didn't plan on sayin' that. I just said it. It popped into my head and I said it. *Drown*. I been dead for over two years now and Pat's learned a thing or two, believe it or not. Before, I wouldn't say nothin' about what I was thinkin'. My thoughts were nobody's damn business. I'd rather punch you in the mouth than let you see what was goin' on inside me.

But I'm learnin' things now I didn't know nothin' about. I'm learning that important things don't just pop into my head out of nowhere. They always come from someplace. It's like there's a string attached to my thoughts. And following that string backwards leads to *something... something*. I dunno, something worth something...*to me*. That's an awful big thought for somebody like me. But I'm startin' to think different than I used to. I'm startin' to think that the ugly dowager's hump in my chest was all them awful things that happened to me balled up into one. And that's got me cogitating. I got a flash, a brainchild that started me thinkin' about if I could melt it. Melt away all those heavy feelings inside my chest.

Listenin' to Kathleen tell about my story about George Washington did somethin' to me. It got me remembering things. It got me remembering about those poor souls marching through ice and snow, usin' rags for shoes. About the bloody footprints. Then I remembered how hearin' that story when I was a little girl melted my heart. And how I hadn't thought about that story until somethin' brought it to my mind and I told it to Kathleen and my heart melted all over again for them poor souls, just like it did when I first heard it. But I didn't say a word to Kathleen about my heart goin' soft. I figured she would just think I was stupid for feeling like cryin' my eyes out over somethin' as dumb as George Washington's soldiers.

I'm startin' to put an awful lot of things together about my life before I died. How I never looked too much outside myself. How I kept myself wrapped pretty tight. How I always had to keep busy. You can't hit a moving target—that's the way I looked at it. If I slowed down, my mind would start racing, hollering at me for how terrible I was. Hollering at me for being so stupid and ugly. If I stood still for too long, my brain would go black and then there'd be Sister Bobby and her long boobs. And her stink. It gave me headaches somethin' terrible, standing still did. The only way I could keep my brain quiet was to keep runnin'. I never had no idea that my thoughts could be different. I never had the idea to argue with my mind. I never thought my mind could be nice to me.

When Kathleen started telling about me and the George Washington story, runnin' away was all I could think about. My head started to squeeze itself and I thought I was gonna pop a blood vessel. I *knew* Kathleen was gonna say awful things about me. I *knew* it sure as I'm sittin' here. *Who does she think she is?*—that's what I was thinkin' when she started that story. I was gonna hightail it out of there faster than you could bat an eyelash. Why should I hang around just to hear my daughter say some ugly crap about me? And you better believe that runnin' away on this side is easy to do.

I don't want to say this wrong, but it's like magic around here. Nobody forces me to do anything I don't want to do. I go wherever I want to go. Do whatever I want to do. But somethin' told me, somethin' in my heart like a whisper or somethin', invited me to stay, real nice like. A real nice voice that melted somethin' in me. Even though I was real scared of what Kathleen was gonna say about me, I thought, *What if I stay here for a little while?* I never believe nothin' good will happen to me—that's just how I am. But I liked that feeling in my heart, that melting feeling. And from bein' around here as long as I have, I knew that if I left—the second I turned away—that melting feeling would leave.

So I stayed and listened to Kathleen tell her story. And I started to feel some things I hardly remember feeling before. Nice things. I felt loose inside, like somethin' came untied. This might not be nice to say, but it felt similar to takin' off my rubber girdle when I was a young woman and I cared about havin' a flat stomach. Maybe you don't know what that's like, but I do. Every day when I got out of that thing, I used to say to myself, *Oh, that feels so good.* That's how I felt listenin' to Kathleen's story: *good.* And I got so wrapped up in it that I started to float. I felt like I sprouted wings. Like I was flying. I felt like I *could* fly. Like a bird. I felt like it would be *possible* for me—for Pat Allen—to fly. I thought about that, *me flying.* ME! Of all people! *Flying!* I never supposed such a thing—*Pat Allen flying.* Pat Allen *free.*

When I was alive, I used to say over and over, *I want my freedom. I just want my freedom.* I was like a broken record sayin' that all the time. And there I was, dead as a doornail, listenin' to a story, and finally feelin' the feelin' of being free. My brain just lifted up. That's the best I can explain. It just lifted up. Like it opened up like a box top, and the sky came in and I felt that dowager's hump inside my chest melt like an ice cube under a water spigot. And then things started to flow out of my mind, like ideas. Good thoughts. Some old dreams I forgot about floated up into the light where I could see them. I thought about how I used to want to be a nurse. My God, I haven't thought about wantin' to be a nurse in fifty years!

You know, I'm not accustomed to bein' happy, but I started feelin' happy. And I decided, *Pat, just let yourself be happy for a minute.* That's a real big deal for me, lettin' myself feel happy. I don't go in for fallin' for nothin' about that happy stuff. I learned the hard way that you can't trust nothin' about bein' happy. Happy will make a fool out of you. It'll punch you in the gut every time. I always killed my happy feelings before they could kill me; that's one of the things I'm puttin' together from my old life.

How the minute I started feelin' happy, I'd make myself get mad. That way, I wouldn't get hurt. I couldn't be disappointed. Around here, they call it protecting yourself. I guess that's what I did—protected myself from gettin' hurt. But with my brain floatin' and my heart feelin' that melty feeling—it felt so good it hurt—I decided to just let myself feel happy for a little while. You know how a dam bursts? That's how it was with my ideas. They just started flooding me in a big circle of light. Showin' me things I *could* do if I had a mind to. Remindin' me of things I always wanted to do. I felt like I had wings. I felt like I could fly. *I wanted to fly.* Like a kite. Like a balloon. A bird. I was so excited!

If I didn't know better, I'd say I was wrapped in an electric blanket. But there wasn't no blanket around me. And I wasn't warm like in the summertime. I wasn't sweatin'. It wasn't a sticky heat. It's hard to describe. I have it now! My *heart* was warm. That's what it was. I was warm in the cockles of my heart. That's when I said to myself, "Pat, somethin's going on," because I had the weird sensation that the warm I was feeling…maybe this is a sin to say…but that feeling, I think, was towards myself. But when I thought that, my brain started arguing, tryin' to tell me how dumb I was for thinkin' I could feel good about myself. And it was only a trick, because an old woman like me doesn't have no business thinkin' about bein' happy. Then I felt myself gettin' cold. And Sister Bobby started sneakin' into my head. I felt her there tappin' her foot in the dark, waitin' to kick my ass for me opening my big mouth and tellin' what she did to me. I started shiverin' so bad. Like when I was waitressin' at Howard Johnson's and the cooks sent me to the meat locker to get steaks. It was so cold in there that my blood froze. That's how I felt. The same way. I was *freezing*. And I could feel that dowager's hump in my chest again like it never left. It was so heavy—heavier than dripping-wet dungarees from the days when I had to use a wringer washer.

My mind kept screaming, *Pat, you belong in Hell. You know you do.* I started drowning…in sorrow. That's the best way I can describe it. No different than from drowning in the Delaware. It was terrible awful. I wouldn't wish nothin' like that on my worst enemy. I was strangling on sadness. I felt like mud was lodged in my chest. I couldn't catch my breath. The wind was knocked out of me. I couldn't see nothin'. I was ice cold. And so scared that my heart stopped. I knew this was the end of the end. There wasn't nothin' more for me. No more chances. I'd reached the bottom of my life. The end of death. Everything was over for good. Hell wasn't hot like they said. It was freezing. I was frozen stiff in a cold Hell. With Sister Bobby in my brain and that dowager's hump in my chest. I couldn't lift a finger. Not one finger. There was no use tryin' to run away no more. I couldn't move. I didn't even have the strength to crawl into a hole. Everything I ever thought about feelin' good was true: *happy don't last*. I fell over. I remember that. I toppled over like a gravestone—crying tears that wouldn't come out—and hit the frozen floor of Hell.

92

Pat

I can't say exactly what happened next. Because I'm not sure. All I can say is there was nothing. I didn't feel nothin'. Not cold, not nothin'. Not sad. I didn't think nothin' about Bobby or nobody else. I didn't see nothin', either. Not even black. But then I woke up. Not like from a sleep. Because I wasn't asleep. I was just *there*, do you follow me?—more compared to a blank stare, but it never hit me that I was staring. Because I didn't feel it. And I wasn't seeing nothin'. I was just *there*, but *there* was *nowhere*. And I didn't know anything until I snapped out of it.

After I snapped out of it, it hit me like a ton of bricks that I was still dead! I never been so excited about anything in my whole life. You gotta realize, I thought I was a real goner. I thought I reached the end—the end of Pat Allen. The end of living. The end of the whole world. I thought I was nothin' but a knocked-over gravestone left out there on the ice. Nothin' but a shriveled, frozen chicken carcass. But I was still here! I was still dead! There's gotta be a better word for dead. But I don't know what it is. All I know is my heart almost burst out of my chest when I realized I wasn't finished for good! Finding out that my mind was still alive! That I was awake! All I kept thinking was that this was better than bein' at a parade with all the drums and baton twirlers and how your heart pounds because you feel so stirred up. I never thought a person could be this worked up! You gotta understand, I met my old friend again. But my old friend was *me*!

After I snapped out of it, that's when I started in with the light. Like a dream lit up from the inside. But not exactly a dream. I guess daydreamin' spells it out, because I wasn't asleep. And I wasn't just starin' into space. Back in the old days, they used to call it wool gathering, I guess. But not that, either. I wasn't trying to figure out a problem. I was seeing moving pictures and having feelings about things, but I was in the lighted-up daydream just like bein' in a room with the lights turned on. *I was part of the daydream*. Part of the movie, I guess you'd say. And I knew it. I felt it. I was myself—Pat—floatin' inside a daydream. Inside a spongy bubble. Slow motion. Yeah, it was sim-u-lar to slow motion. Nothin' fast, nothin' hurried about it. I coulda been floatin' on a raft in our pool on Mark Twain Drive back in the '60s. Only I was standing...sort of...maybe walking, I'm not sure...in the center, in the middle of the light all around me. And the strange thing was, my thinkin' and my daydreamin' all blended together real smooth, like a pudding. That's a good way to put it. I was there inside a creamy pudding with the low beams on. That strikes me funny, *pudding with the low beams on*. But honest to god that's what it felt like, smooth and creamy. There wasn't no rough spots. I was inside my mind and inside my feelings at the same time. Slow watching. Just hanging there, feelin' like Pat, only a relaxed Pat. That's the best I can say. Maybe that don't make sense to you. But that's how it was. I explain things kind of funny, don't I?

Soft as a pillow, that's what stands out for me. Real soft was all around me. I didn't feel scared. I don't know why. But I didn't. That's what I remember: *I didn't feel scared*. I don't remember a time in my whole life when I didn't feel scared of somethin'. Not that I knew it when I was livin'. But with the softness, that's when I realized how scared I always been. That's a strange thing to not know about—bein' scared your whole life. *Livin' in fear*, that's what they call it around here. I never knew what they were talking about. And I never asked, because I figured it didn't have nothin' to do with me. But I started to wonder about things with that softness makin' me feel real calm. I started thinkin' there might be somethin' to all that stuff I never knew nothin' about. Maybe all that calm stuff, all that feelin' good wasn't just a bunch of malarkey.

But just as sure as I said that—soon as those words left my mouth— I started gettin' nervous. And my toes started gettin' cold. Real, real cold. I could feel them shivers takin' up and I was tryin' to hold them back. I felt Sister Bobby bust into my head again, black as the ace of spades. And that thick dowager's hump startin' to grow back. That's when I started losin' my mind. It started goin' crazy, runnin' in circles. Pullin' me toward that Hell ice. And the toppled-over gravestone. All I could think of was frostbite. My toes were gonna rot and fall off from frostbite. Freezing needles bein' shoved under my toenails, that's what it felt like. I kept sayin' to myself, "Pat, you're off your rocker. This isn't *real.*"

But if it wasn't real, why could I *see* my dried-up old corpse laying out there on that ice? Gray. Frozen. Stiff as a board. And oh, good grief, the laughing...the cackling... I was locked up in a bughouse, *I had to be*—only crazy people in straitjackets hear cackling comin' out of nowhere...comin' from everywhere. *It's over for me for good now*, that's what I thought. *I'm nothin' but a crackpot.* I felt myself goin' down. Sliding back into Hell with my eyeballs froze wide open. The cackling was ripping me, ripping me apart at the seams. My ears were ringing, it was so loud. Howling everywhere. Ghosts. Witches' cackling. I don't know what it was. The screams of witches. That's just what it sounded like. Like it was from the movies. Except I couldn't see no bodies. But with my eyeballs froze wide open like that, I could *see* the cackling right in front of my eyes. And that scared me somethin' terrible, because I was *seein'* noise. That don't make sense, but that's the only way to describe it. How could cackling take up a shape? How could it be something you could see? Something you could touch? I can't get over it. I can't get my head to think about it right, but if I'm lying, you can shoot me: that cackling was hanging right in front of my face lookin' an awful lot like icicles frozen in midair. Just hanging there like they was nailed to a wall. But there wasn't no wall. And they was...I'm tryin' to get the words...jiggling or fidgeting...shaking. It made me think of flames how they flicker, only the icicles weren't givin' off light. They were givin' off these screeches, these cackling echoes that wouldn't stop.

I'm tired somethin' awful tryin' to explain how it was. All that screeching, that cackling echoing all over the place. I might as well been inside a metal bucket bein' banged with sticks and stones for all the racket. I'll never forget none of it. Not the noise. Not the frostbite. Not in a million years. And I'll never forget them fidgeting icicles, just like witches fingers, pointing right at me.

93

Pat

There was nothin' else for me to think but that I was off my rocker. A lunatic from the insane asylum. That finally after everything I been through, it was all over. The rest of it was nothin' but Hell. Just like they said. I was goin' to Hell and I wouldn't be comin' back this time. I been hard up before, but not hard up like this. I was more than hard up. I'm tryin' to get you to understand that I reached the end of *me*. The end of Pat. The last page in the book. There wasn't nothin' else left. It was over. The end of my story. I was finished. Nothin' else to think about. There wasn't nothin' left inside me to run to. My mind was turned inside out. Everything was ruined. I was just the gnawed chicken bones they throw in the garbage bag after supper. There wasn't no me to hold together no more. I was washed up. Shrunk as far back in myself as I could go. Any further and I woulda left myself and been somethin' else. Maybe a tree. Or a dog. Do you read me? I was flat up against the skin inside my own back. The brick wall where I ended. After that, Pat didn't exist. There wasn't nothin' else.

But then somethin' happened. Somethin' came over me. Somethin' whipped up inside me. Somethin' I never felt before. Somethin' bigger than I can explain right. The only word I can think is *rush*—a rush came over me. No... *blaze*...that's it. A hot blaze like you get when you swallow a juice glass full of vodka. Only a lot bigger. *A lot*. But nothin' like gettin' all riled up over somethin' you're mad about, like I used to do all the time. This was different. Somethin' told me this...*this blaze*...was important. And it felt *great*. I don't go around sayin' I feel great. That's not my style. But I'm sayin' it now—*I felt great!* Not like bein' tipsy. Better than that. And not like bein' mad enough to spit wooden nickels, either. Bigger than that. Oh, it's so hard to explain.

It felt...*stunning. That's the word.* Kathleen always used to say that:

stunning. I love that word. But I never had nothing to use it for. *Stunning.* That's what it felt like: *stunning.* Because my heart felt like it swelled up as big as a red moon. A big moon rising right inside my chest. Bigger than a helium balloon in the Macy's Thanksgiving Day parade. Hot as blazes. Light as a feather. But solid... Rock solid as a wrestler's muscle—you don't know that I used to know Hulk Hogan, do you? He let me feel his muscles once. What do you think of that? He was a dingbat, but his muscles were hard as rock. That's how I know about wrestler's muscles. And that's what I had. A blazing, rock-solid wrestler's muscle floating around inside my chest, light as a feather.

I still can't get over it. Nothin' like this ever happened to me. I never had a light heart before. My heart always felt sore, full of mud and splinters. It was so heavy sometimes that I didn't know how I was gonna walk around. But this new moon heart—blazing in my chest, floatin' like some kind of balloon—felt stronger than anything I ever felt. I coulda moved a mountain if I wanted. I never felt so good. Not in my whole life. After all these years, my heart felt good. It felt...*right.* It fit me. It wasn't nervous. It wasn't sad no more. It didn't hurt like it always did. It didn't put the squeeze on me. It didn't make me feel mean and ugly.

Then it came over me that this moon heart was my *real* heart. My cleaned-out heart. It got me thinkin' about baseboards after I took bleach to them and scrubbed away the grime. And the walls I fresh painted when I got a brainstorm to do some decorating. And cleaning out closets. I used to stand back and admire what I did with that feeling... I don't know—satisfaction, I guess you would say—from everything lookin' brand new and spotless. That's how my heart felt: brand new and spotless. Clean. I couldn't get over how fresh the air that I was breathing tasted. I couldn't get over my clean-feeling heart. That it really belonged to me. That it was really mine. I didn't understand it. But it was there in my chest, feeling swelled up like I had blue ribbons pinned on my blouse, and strong as a red moon, beating time like a marching drum. I'm tryin' to explain this right without getting it confused. I was mad without bein' pissed off. It *felt like* anger running through me, but instead of making me mad, it made me feel surefooted. And spunky. But not mean and bratty. I wanted to tap dance.

I remember saying to myself, *Pat, you feel like a queen. You finally feel like a real queen.* Ever since I can remember, I wanted to feel like a queen. Just once in my life, I wanted to wear a long, flowy dress and glide down a big staircase and wave to everybody like I was the Queen of England. That's all I ever asked. But nothin' like that ever happened to me. And here bein' dead, it was happening right in my own heart. My dead heart was more alive than when I was living. It was making me feel beautiful. I couldn't get over it. Feeling like a queen in my own heart. And do you want to know something? I felt like it was in the cards the whole time. That was weird. To have a hunch that the whole time, I was a beautiful person, a good person, only I never knew it. *I never knew it.*

I had to cogitate on that: *I never knew I was a good person when I was alive.* Yet it stands to reason that my good, clean heart musta been inside me all the time. I just never saw it, but it was always there. There was a *good Pat.* I got so excited about that. You coulda told me I just won the million-dollar lottery. I swear, I heard quarters spitting out of a slot machine. I wanted to jump for joy. Me, Pat Allen—the whole time I was a good person! I thought I was worthless. And I wasn't! In all my life, I never knew what it was like to fit like a glove inside my own body. I never knew what it was like to feel like I belonged…to anything. I always felt separate. Like I lived behind some kind of wall…a glass wall…and I didn't know how to reach through it. I couldn't touch what I wanted to touch. That's the only way to explain it. But with this new clean feeling in my heart, the wall…it dissolved. That's what I think. It kind of dissolved, and that's when it came to me that I *do* belong to something. *I belong to myself.*

I can't describe feeling lonely in your own body. That you don't really live there. Feelin' so much hate for yourself. Feeling like you're a nobody. Like a piece of garbage. But when the wall dissolved and my heart was making me feel like I was somebody important, things changed for me. I don't know how that happened. I can't explain it right…but my heart made me feel that I meant something to myself. I never felt soft for myself. I never felt like I belonged anywhere, least of all inside my own heart.

And I'll never forget what came next. I don't know if I can put it into words—my arms, my hands...they were glowing. And tingling. It made me think of holding lightning in a bottle. And my legs...I had the sense that I was standing on top of the Rock of Gibraltar. High up. Maybe Pikes Peak. I can't do justice to what I saw—how my eyes were looking right through things. How everything was transparent. And I could see all the way through whatever I thought about: people, houses, oceans, hearts. Everything was crystal clear, see-through. Nothing was hid. All I had to do was look and I could see. Whatever I wanted to look at was clear as the windows I used to Windex. Maybe it was a miracle, I don't know. But there I was, on top of the world, looking around. My moon heart swelled inside my chest. Tingling with shock...electricity. Feeling like a *queen*. I can't get over it. I can't get over any of it. Most of all, I can't get over feeling like a queen. Me. Pat Allen. A queen.

That's when things really started to dawn on me. I'd say it's sim–u–lar to watching the moon rise real slow. I felt myself turning. Not in circles. But changing direction, I guess you could say. Real calm-like I felt my mind turn around. And right in front of my eyes was a moonbeam, and then I heard my heart talk as if it was talkin' out loud. Maybe that don't make sense to you. But a lot of things don't make sense around here compared to before. All I can say is what happened. And I'm tellin' you, my heart talked to me. *It's time for a decision, Pat,* it said clear as day. And I didn't hang around hemming and hawing. I just stepped forward into the moonbeam. And as soon as I did, I knew plain as plain can be that I'd made the right decision, because that moonbeam fell over me like a halo. It reached all the way down to the ground and warmed me from my toes all the way up.

That's when I started to come to the conclusion that just because things don't look and feel the same as I'm used to don't mean they're not real. But then my mind started to get a little shaky and I thought, *Pat, why aren't you all shook up about invisible things bein' real as things that look familiar?* I felt that awful pull of my mind wantin' to think like that. Wantin' to ruin things for me. But I said, *That's enough of that, Pat.* Somethin' came over me when I said that to myself, and cross my heart, I felt warm as toast. You know, I couldn't stand butter my whole life, not even the thought of it, but there I was melting like butter on toast over what I said to myself.

Then a brainwave passed through me almost like a dream, sayin', *Pat, this feels like love.* I couldn't believe somethin' like that would ever cross my mind, that I could ever care for myself. But it felt real good. It felt *real* good. I felt like I wasn't just dumb, stupid "Pat the Waitress" servin' steaks to a bunch of fat moneybags. I felt like *someone.* Someone who meant something. Someone who *meant* something to myself. I didn't feel like Pat no more. I felt like *Mary Patricia.* My real name fit. My name, *Mary Patricia*, fit me.

My spirits lifted. My words lifted. My world lifted.

94

Mary Patricia

Mary Patricia. Mary Patricia. I never realized what a beautiful name that was. I never knew that my real name meant anything to me until I heard my heart whisper it. They never called me Mary Patricia. They always called me Patsy or Pat. But hearing my real name said in my heart like that was music to my ears. It sounded like a poem. I could've been taking a warm bath the way it lifted my spirits. It made me feel good about myself. I'm not accustomed to that. It's hard to explain, but I saw myself different when my heart called me *Mary Patricia.* Dumb Pat wasn't looking back at me from the mirror anymore. *Dumb, Can't-Do-It Pat* peeled away. Like a scab.

I never knew that something not worth worrying about like a name could make you feel like you have wings. They used to say, "You can call me anything, but don't call me late for dinner." I didn't think what you called somebody—or what you called yourself—mattered. I never knew that my real name mattered to me until I heard my heart say it. The only thing I can imagine is it's like wearing too-tight shoes that squish your toes. You get used to them. You never complain. Then one day you get a pair that fits and your feet feel like they can fly.

I'm thinking that there's a way about a person's name that I never knew. The way it's used. How people say it. How it hurts when it doesn't fit. How they can make it sound like a cussword. Or like they're lowering themselves to speak to you. Sometimes I felt like my name left a sour taste in people's mouths. For a lot of years, nobody said my name with love. When I started to get old, *Pat* turned ugly on me. It wasn't cute or fun anymore from like when I was young and feisty. I guess *I* wasn't cute and fun anymore. And I hated that something terrible. Maybe that's part of it. I lost my looks. I'd started drinking. Then I came around to thinking that *Pat* was going to end up an old bag lady. Nobody could convince me any different. *Pat the Bag Lady.* Nobody wanting her around. No place to live except in one of her children's dirty cellars, if they'd even have her. That scared me something awful. Being treated like garbage. Feeling like garbage. *Pat* was old. Shriveled up like a prune. Unwelcome. I despised the thought of *Pat.* I didn't know I was anything else but *Pat.*

Then all this happened and my heart told me who I really was, who I always was—*Mary Patricia*—I just didn't know it. My name touched something in me. It hit the spot. It calmed me. My nerves melted. I felt my backbone. It made me want to stand up straight. I wasn't tired any-more. My heart showed me my reflection and I looked beautiful. Then my heart told me that I could fly. And I started to feel it. I started to believe it.

Mary Patricia. What a beautiful name.

95

Mary Patricia

It's time for a decision...Mary Patricia. Weird how those words kept hanging around me, ringing in my ears. Nothing like the tinnitus I suffered from when I was alive. Those words sounded like a pretty nice invitation. That's why I didn't get aggravated and I just listened to them. I didn't feel like they were trying to trick me. They felt soft. Like a hug. And that made me want to mull them over. I felt like they were singing to me. A lullaby. How a mother would sing a lullaby to her baby. How I used to sing to Kathleen when she was little and nobody was around to make me feel funny about it.

Being so relaxed, I think, let certain things come into my mind—things I never wanted to bother thinking about when I was alive. Like making decisions. I always hated making decisions. I guess because I couldn't trust myself. How could I? I *always* made the wrong one. I always felt so stupid, a real dum-dum. I figured everybody knew more than me, knew what was best. Anyway, what difference did it make who made my decisions? I was never going to get what I wanted anyhow. It was less hassle to let other people tell me what to do; then I always had somebody else to blame when nothing worked out for me.

But then out of the blue it occurred to me that it must've seemed like every time I turned around, I was pestering people with, "What should I do? I don't know what to do." If I had a penny for every time I bugged somebody to tell me what I should do, I would've died a rich woman. That's when it struck me. *Pat, you did more than ask about what you should do: you made people make your decisions for you.* That took the wind out of me, and I had to stop for a minute and catch my breath. Right then and there, I decided to escape while the escaping was good, because I didn't want to think about any of that. I was gearing up to run for my life when I saw myself sitting on a little grass hill beside a pond, just staring into the water. And here's where it's really weird: I really was sitting on a hill watching water flow.

That's the way it is around here. I don't understand it very well, because things happen in the darnedest ways than from what I'm used to. One minute you're here, the next minute you're somewhere else. The only way I can explain it is to say you're on your couch watching television in the middle of winter but in your mind you're a million miles away on the beach in Florida. The big difference around here is that you actually go to Florida. Not just in your mind, either. And you don't need a car. I'm still learning about how all this stuff operates, but I'm taking to it.

As I sat on that hill staring at the pond, my heart started to fill up from everything being so peaceful. I couldn't get over how suddenly everything meant so much to me. The grass, smelling like it was just mowed. And the birds. I never really listened to birds when I was alive. The chirping was really nice. The water had a sound too. A swishing sound. And the breeze was so mild. I remember it on my cheeks. I noticed something else, too—something in the air. I tried to figure it out. It was a sort of feeling in the air. And it touched me in the way that light touches you, only I couldn't see it. I finally realized it was kindness. I can't explain it, but there was kindness all around me. I was sitting in kindness. I sat there for a long time just feeling it. It was so different from the air I lived in when I was alive. The air around me then hurt. It made my heart sore.

At first I thought I was daydreaming when I saw the bubbles...soap bubbles the kind kids blow from those plastic wands. But common sense told me that it wasn't a daydream, since they were floating all around me. And I could see all the colors of the rainbow coming from them clear as day. Pink. Blue. And all the rest. I was hypnotized by how they sparkled in the sunlight. It took me back to a long time ago, to my kids laughing when they were little. I remember thinking, *I could get used to this, sitting here watching bubbles, dreaming about nice things, feeling good.*

The thought occurred to me, *Is this heaven? If it is, I'd like to stay here forever.* I sat there for a long, long time. I don't remember how long. Time is different around here from what I'm used to. It didn't feel like a long time, but I know it was. Maybe it was a year in your time. All I know is that I sat there until I had my fill. Until I was filled up. But not heavy like after a big meal. Filled up and light at the same time — contented. That's the word: *contented*.

I'd been hankering to touch one of those bubbles since I first noticed them floating in front of my face, but I didn't exactly have the will, since I was enjoying myself so much as it was. And I guess I didn't want to break the spell, either. But then I started to get a little antsy, so I figured, what the heck? And I reached out and touched one. It felt like satin, just as I guessed it would...as smooth as a baby's behind. That's when oddball things started happening. It's not easy to explain. And I guess you'd have to have been there to understand it, but there was a thought...a memory... inside that bubble. *And it belonged to me.* The only place I've ever seen thought-bubble things is in comic strips. I never had a mind to think they could ever be *real*. But like I keep telling you, I'm getting used to how it goes around here, and it's a lot different from what I'm accustomed to. As soon as I touched that bubble, the memory inside it melted over me. It made me think about putting on a velvet dress. How it feels on your skin. Really soft and silky. Kind of how Jell-O feels after it's set up and you run your finger across the top.

The weird thing about it is that the memory was a *bad one*. It had nothing to do with happy times. I started getting confused over that. Because in my old life, when something terrible about myself popped into my mind, I'd feel like... like I was going to blow up. Or drown. And I'd feel my heart squeeze into a tiny stone and roll down a black hole, leaving me alone. Some other Pat took over when that happened. She'd have a conniption fit and want to slap somebody across the face. Or cry until she dried up. Or go hide somewhere and drink until she couldn't remember why she was so upset.

But this was different. The memory wasn't different — it reminded me how stupid I was. How embarrassed I was over all the things I did wrong. How useless I felt. How I failed at everything I tried to do. How dejected and alone I felt because nobody could stand being around me.

How ashamed I was about people just putting up with me. It was the same kind of memory that always made me so miserable—but everything around it *felt* different. It's hard to explain. But the air was *kind*. And I felt like I was inside a soft velvet dress. Then I started thinking about *Mary Patricia*. I thought about how my name made me feel warm and beautiful. I thought about how much I liked feeling good. I took a deep breath—I remember the air smelled just like how my sheets used to when I hung them outside to dry—and thought to myself, *What if I stood up to those bad memories?*

I don't know where I got the nerve to even think that; I must've been feeling softhearted toward myself. Maybe it was the kindness in the air making me feel calm. All I know is that I didn't feel nervous. And here's another oddball thing: somehow the thought of having the gumption to go eyeball to eyeball with my bad memories made me *feel* my backbone. My heart jumped over that, over not having my backbone feel like a wet dishrag. I felt so happy, *so brave*; I tried it again to see if it was real and not just a dirty trick. So I put that thought into words I said out loud: *Mary Patricia, you can stand up to those bad memories.* And everything *was* real. Realer than real. *Good grief, my backbone actually vibrated.* I couldn't get over it, my backbone vibrating. As true as I'm standing here, I tell you I felt electricity run up and down my spine when I said those words out loud. Electricity. That's what it felt like. Electricity inside my blood. In my bones. On my skin. *A current.* That's it. A current of electricity in my body, in my backbone. I never felt such a thing before.

I'm going to do it, I said to myself. I decided I was going to try to look at those bad memories, try to figure them out. I *decided* to take a chance. It didn't occur to me until a long time after that I—*Mary Patricia*—made *a decision*. A real decision. My own decision. I was so happy about that.

96

Mary Patricia

One by one, slow as molasses, other thoughts and memories drifted toward me in satin bubbles and took up like velvet on my skin. They spelled themselves out like words typed on a page in a book that I could read and understand. And contemplate without wanting to do myself in. Even though none of it was what you would call good. I've always liked things arranged nice, and seeing memories all neat and organized that way and feeling the kindness in the air helped me not get too nervous. It sure wasn't a picnic, but I stayed calm and read every word one at a time.

At first I didn't know what the fog meant. It sat all around me like a tent. It wasn't wet or heavy; it didn't even move. It was just quiet, cloudy stuff I couldn't see through. Now, I have enough sense to know that around here, *something always means something.* And if I didn't get all riled up, if I could keep my blood pressure down, sooner or later I would start getting the hint. So I blew out just like I was finishing up a Raleigh from my smoking days and let my shoulders fall. That felt good. It wasn't easy for me; I'm not the kind of person that is good at relaxing, but I made up my mind, and when I make up my mind, nothing can change it. That's from my old Pat days. But I didn't feel like the old Pat. She was mad a lot. I wasn't mad about the fog and sitting in it. Nobody forced me to stay there—I made my own decision to sit there and try to relax. After a while it started to feel good. It felt better than good. It's like I was sitting in the middle of patience.

That was new for me. My mind turned off to worry. Taking the time to sit still. Not thinking about anything. Not thinking was the best part. My mind got a chance to take a break. It was like it was getting aired out. Housewives used to do that—you know—air things out. Blankets. Pillows. Rugs. I used to take winter coats outside and hang them on the clothesline and let the sunshine freshen them up. That's what was going on with me:

I was getting freshened up, but in the fog. Maybe sharpened up is a better way to say it. Because I wasn't feeling dull. Even though I was in a fog. I was sitting in a fog, but the fog wasn't sitting in me—not like when I was alive. It was weird feeling my wits sharpen. As sharp as a tack, that's what they used to say. I'm not used to that, but I liked it. I like feeling sharp. As crisp as a cracker.

97

Mary Patricia

I never got involved with what was going on around me back when I was alive. I always took a backseat, let everybody else take charge. Things are different around here. Nobody takes charge for you. I've learned that. I could sit on my duff until the cows came home if I wanted to and nobody would bat an eye. The difference now is that I don't want to. There are things here for me to learn—things I never knew about. Things that make sense. Things that are important to me. Things I'm interested in. I'm on cloud nine about that. It's a shot in the arm, my mind being so alive. So, I wasn't afraid of the fog. I knew there was something in it for me. I just waited.

Did you ever hear the expression *deer in the headlights*? That's the best way I can describe how I started to feel. Something not right started creeping over me. Something from the air. Nothing I could see. Or hear. But something there in the fog was touching me. Not touching my skin. Touching my instincts. I didn't like it. Because it was too familiar. Bad familiar. Like a terrible stomach bug. My hands started to shake and my stomach lurched all the way up into my throat. "Oh no," I remember thinking, "not this again." Same as thinking you're finally done with throwing up, then out of nowhere, your stomach starts rumbling again and you're back hanging over the toilet. I could feel whatever it was closing in on me, crawling inside my heart. A wet blanket. A real spoilsport, ruining my mood. Ruining everything for me.

Why is this happening to me? Why? Why?, I kept asking myself over and over. Why after how good I was feeling, how good I was doing? I thought all the bad stuff was over and done with. Gone, forever. I thought I was finally *free*. But the wet blanket feeling wouldn't leave. It kept bringing back bad memories like they never left. Memories that I wanted kept locked away. Ones about me being stupid. And worse...

Terrible awful words hollered in my mind. Words I don't want to repeat. Disgusting thoughts screamed inside my head. The worst thoughts I could imagine—gunshots to the heart. Killing me. Telling me who I really was and always would be—the worst, lowest woman to ever walk the face of the earth. I felt like I was a little girl again drowning in the Delaware River. I felt like a crippled old woman drowning inside that dowager's hump that stood in for a heart. And it ached something terrible, my heart did. I'd had it. I couldn't take anymore. My nerves snapped like a rubber band, and I turned into a spitfire right then and there and conjured up *Pat*. With every last bit of the old Pat I could muster, I spit into that fog and screamed at the top of my lungs, *I take back everything I ever said about wanting to learn things around here. I'm leaving! For good! And I'm never coming back. I'm going to sit on my fat duff and pray that the cows never come home.*

Nobody crossed Pat. In my day, I was *known* for my sass—for biting off my nose to spite my face so fast that I could make your head spin. I yelled into that fog like a banshee and I didn't care. I didn't care if God *Himself* flew out of His heaven and bawled me out in person for being such a brazen hussy. He could kick me into purgatory for all I cared. Send me packing straight to Hell. I didn't give a damn. What do you people say nowadays, *bring it on?* That's what I wanted: God Himself to bring it on. Because I was ready. Dukes up. Thumb my nose. When He came to give me what was coming, I'd spit in his face. I'd slice Him in two with my comeback. Do or die, I'd have the final say. I'd tell Him that I wanted to go back to the old Pat. That I was sick to death of *Mary Patricia*—the goody two-shoes. I'd dare *Himself* to send me to Hell. *I want to go.* That's what I would tell Him. *I want to be a shriveled-up old corpse. I want to spend all eternity—every single last second until the end of time—out there on the ice, frozen as stiff as a board.* Nobody messes with Pat. I don't care if you are God Himself. Pat Allen would have her say.

I waited for the ax to fall. And waited. Tapping my foot. Rehearsing my speech. Making sure it would sting. Making sure I'd hit the jugular. Nothing. I waited some more, glaring into the mist, making dares. Not a peep. Nothing. Just silence. And me. In the fog. Killing time. Dealing with a wet dowager's hump in my chest and the dry heaves knocking at my door. Practicing my lines. Then suddenly thunder. *Thunder? Where did that come from?* Not from the outside. No God rushing down from on high throwing lightning bolts at my head. Still, *thunder.* Booming. As loud as a drum in a parade. Deep. Pounding. Growing inside. A storm. But *not* a storm. A presence. *An authority.* Inside me. My heart thundering. Beating strong. And stronger. Muscle. Inside a core. The fighting tree inside the bark. Thunder heart. Fighting heart. Beating from deep inside. Louder. Stronger. Thunder woken up. Feet hitting the floor. A motor with a tiger in the tank. *Thundering.* Then slowing down. Into a hum. Purring like a brand new Singer sewing machine. Humming and purring inside my skin. My bones. Rippling my blood. A low, steady bass. Sturdy. Full. As rich as chocolate pudding. *Smooth, echoing thunder.* What happened next I have no earthly explanation for.

98

Mary Patricia

A figure appeared. Right in front of me. A living, breathing woman. As alive as anybody I've ever seen. If I'd had a stethoscope, I could've proven it. *Fatima*. That's what I thought about right away. *Mary* appearing to a bunch of kids on a foggy mountain somewhere in one of those overly religious countries. I was devoted to the Blessed Mother when I was alive. I even made the pilgrimage to Tampa to see her image on the side of a ritzy office building there. You pulled up into a big parking lot and there she was, huge. Taller than a billboard. Bigger than on a screen at a drive-in movie. A miracle had painted her likeness across the windows all the way up to the roof. You couldn't see her face, but she looked like she was made out of a rainbow because of all the colors. There was no shade and I was baking in the hot Florida sun, but I recited the rosary anyhow, despite the sweat running down my face.

I stared at the woman in the fog, trying to figure out then if it was *Mary* come down to see me. Maybe all those rosaries were finally paying off. Anyway, who else could it be? I felt like I knew her, but I couldn't place her. I looked her up and down. She was tall. Taller than any woman I'd ever seen. And she had antlers. That was the strange part. *Antlers*. They reminded me of antennas. Lots of them. Going every which way, reaching far, far up. So high they that disappeared into the fog. The way I figured it, it was some kind of fancy halo. That made sense to me. Only thing is, she wasn't dressed like the Blessed Mother from all those pictures and prayer cards. She didn't look anything like the image on the office building.

This woman wore a long sackcloth dress, hand-stitched. I could tell it was handmade from all my years of sewing. And instead of a belt, a thick braided rope was wrapped around her waist and hung all the way down to her feet. I remember thinking, *poor soul*, because burlap is pretty hard on the skin and that rope must've weighed an awful lot. I noticed her toenails—her feet were bare. They were polished. Fire engine red. So were her fingernails. And I thought it was awfully funny that she had on red lipstick, too. She reminded me of someone.

The woman kept staring at me. It seems to me I should've been scared, or aggravated, but I wasn't. I just kept staring back at her, trying to work things out about who she was. I thought about asking her if the name Jesus rang a bell. But then I thought, what was the use? Everybody knows Jesus. Next I thought about giving my sick-and-tired, fed-up speech. I'd practiced it hard enough. But all those great lines I'd rehearsed didn't want to come out. They felt flat. Deflated. Like a used balloon. There wasn't any place for them. The air was too full of what I would have to call kindness. Peace, I guess. That made me confused. I expected a fight.

Something about her took me in. Not in a queer way—I don't go in for that stuff. But she looked, I guess you would say, friendly. She had a friendly look in her eyes. Much different from the stuck-up look in regular people's eyes. She stood up straight, too, held herself to her full height. I liked that. She wasn't slouching. In my good days, I never slouched. I practiced walking with library books on my head. I learned to stand straight and walk correctly, one foot right in front of the other. I balanced a lot of food trays when I waitressed, walking like that. And I never dropped one plate. Not one. I'm proud of that. I was pretty strong in my day. I cogitated on that. How I felt hoisting those heavy trays. How my body felt so healthy. I remember the muscles in my arms. I was proud of them. I was a little thing, but I lifted trays that probably weighed more than I did.

It's weird. The woman spoke to me, but not in words. It's hard to explain, but I detected in her eyes that she was trying to give me a message. Call it a hunch. A gut feeling. It sounds nuts, but this whole world I'm stuck in right now is nuts. I don't have anything else to hold on to, nothing else to go by except what I'm feeling. That's it. I'm feeling my way through the unknown in this place. Feelings are all I have. That's the only way I know that I'm still me. Everything's changed for me. Even my name. And there isn't anybody to tell me what to do. I'm learning to lean on myself. Around here, they call it *trusting your instincts*. I never trusted myself when I was alive. It's hard, I'll tell you.

I knew something was up when the fog started to feel heavier. The doldrums started coming over me. A gray feeling I've always known and could never shake but could never put my finger on. It's nagged me for as far back as I can remember. Not a whole feeling. Not all the way angry or all the way down in the dumps. More like a ghost feeling. A sense. There but not there. An inkling of a feeling is a good way to put it. Wink and it was gone. Wink and it came back again. I could never quite get a hold of it. Like a whisper in the next room. A dream fading as soon as you try to put it into words. It would pester me like a rash that's cleared up but still itches once in a while but there's nothing to scratch. You know how a tiny burr gets stuck in your sock and drives you bananas? But you can't find the darn thing? It was just there, that gray feeling. It came and went with the wind. No rhyme or reason. One minute I'd be as happy as a clam, the next minute a pall would sink my heart.

When I was alive, I never thought there was anything to surmise about my heart sinking like it did out of nowhere. For pity's sake, you don't do a lot of cogitating about the air you breathe, do you? I never did, at least. I just breathed it. How could I ever work out something when I didn't know there was anything to work out? I spent most my life raising kids and cleaning house. That's all I ever knew. How could I figure out something I couldn't point to? You can't see a pall. You can't see electricity, either—I don't know where it lives or how it gets where it's supposed to go. All I know is that when I put a plug in a wall, the light comes on.

I never paid much mind to things I couldn't see. Feelings weren't good for anything. They just made you miserable. That's the way I saw it. I never expected to change my way of thinking. But that's what happened due to the woman in the fog.

99

Mary Patricia

There was something about how the woman in the fog stared at me. And me not getting aggravated over it. It started me thinking that maybe there were grounds for that ghost feeling that I didn't know about. Maybe turning my back on it wasn't the thing to do. But then my nerves started in on me and I warned myself that curiosity killed the cat—that's how I was brought up: you don't ask questions, because *curiosity killed the cat.* I was no dum-dum. I knew what that meant. Curiosity would kill you. That's what I was taught. And that's what I believed. But somehow, looking into the eyes of the woman in the fog made me remember about my kids, how they never took that warning seriously. They'd just sass me and say, *But satisfaction brought her back.* Funny how that smart-aleck remark from all those years ago showed up in my mind and made sense to me.

So I decided to take a chance, and I put my head to concentrating. And straight into my mind popped my dictionary. And that took me back to doing crosswords and how I always looked up definitions for words I didn't know. That's when it hit me. What if the ghost feeling was part of a game—like cards or a crossword puzzle—that I never learned how to play? Crosswords have clues. But you have to figure out the exact words to fit in the little squares. What if the ghost feeling was a clue? What if it was trying to *spell out* something? But instead of words for clues it used a foreign lingo—something as confusing as pig Latin—that had to be un-scrambled before you could understand it? What if the ghost feeling was more than just the regular feelings like I'm used to?

If you want to know the truth, I'm accustomed to feeling sick and tired. I could give you a list of all my aches and pains, from sciatica to bad feet to diabetes...and that's just the beginning... What if that awful ghost feeling around my heart was a real clue to a puzzle itching to be solved? And what if I could solve it? In all my days, I never thought of digging into such a thing as a *feeling*—who cares about feelings, so what was the point? Anyhow, it's not like you could read the instructions or use a dictionary. Then it came to me how proud I was of myself when I finished a whole crossword puzzle. I felt myself putting down the pencil from filling in the last word and relaxing back in my recliner, thrilled to death about my accomplishment. It was like a glow, that feeling. The exact opposite of the gray feeling. What if that ghost feeling was a *real* Chinese puzzle? Then wouldn't it be the cat's meow if I could solve it? I started to get jazzed over that.

But then I asked myself, how could feelings mean anything outside of what you are feeling? An idiot steps on your toe and it hurts. That's the feeling. That's the end of it. What else could there be besides a sore toe? My head started to ache something terrible and that pall took a turn for the worse. It was too confusing. I'm an old dead woman. How could I be expected to figure all this out? Then, just like that, it got simple. The jigsaw puzzle pieces started to fall into place.

Feeling cold tells you to put on a coat. Feeling hungry tells you to eat something. That surmise hammered into my thick skull that it's only common sense that the ghost feeling was trying to tell me *something*. And it was high time I learned to listen. But what was it saying, for Pete's sake? I pictured myself sewing on my old Singer. I never took one lesson. I learned how to use that machine by myself. And I taught myself how to read patterns. Believe me, it was darn hard, because lines and darts were all over the place, going everywhere, and didn't make any sense until I made myself sit still and concentrate. I sewed up a lot of clothes in my time. Cloth dolls, too. I crocheted afghans and cross-stitched pillows. I made quilts. I did it all on my own. Never asked anybody for help. When I was alive, I didn't think what I made was any good. But looking at it all now, I see that I had a real knack. I see how much I loved paying attention to all the little details. I see now that I taught myself to do all those things because my heart was in it. I made all those things because it made my heart happy.

I smiled at the woman in the fog. She smiled back at me.

100

Mary Patricia

Standing there smiling at the woman in the fog, I have to say, my heart was a helium balloon. It could've floated right out of my chest and I wouldn't have been surprised. I couldn't tell you for sure, but I guess that's what lighthearted feels like. When I was alive, I made it a practice to smile a lot—people like people that smile—but I never felt what you would call lighthearted. I learned to hold back. I never got close to people. I'd compare myself to them and always come up with the short end of the stick. So what was there to feel lighthearted about?

Looking in the eyes of the woman in the fog, though, I realized something important. I realized that maybe I'd found what I'd been searching for my whole life on earth. I hardly have the words for it. It's that feeling you get when a little baby kisses you. Warm and fuzzy, I suppose. Elated, maybe? What I'm trying to say is that you don't feel rejected. I guess I would say that you feel loved. But more than that. It's like a mustard plaster on a sore back. It's like the baby reached out and touched your sore heart and you reached back and cuddled her. And you both smiled. So you get the chills up and down your arms because of how it feels...*so good*. And by how that feeling thaws your arthritic bones, you know that the baby has eyes *for you*. And you feel like a million bucks. You feel like you're *somebody—that you count*. And you can bet your life that the baby isn't going to go behind your back and gossip about you like you're a dog. Or ask you for money.

I'm trying to drum up the dictionary words for what I've been searching for my whole life. All I can come up with besides love is...*devotion*. Having the kind of devotion that melts your heart. Where people see you. And really hear you. Where you know that you really matter—*cherished* is a good word. When I was alive, people just tolerated me. They put up with me until they could find an excuse to get away. I could sense it. I saw it in their eyes. It made me feel terrible awful. And in spite of how hard I tried to be friendly by making jokes and paying compliments, no matter how nice I tried to be, they always took me wrong and that made things worse. And then all the lights went out and there I was alone, a stranger in a room full of people I knew.

There's something else I have to say about the woman in the fog. She didn't look at me like I was *poor mom* or *poor Pat*. That used to gall me when they treated me like I was a sad-sack cripple who couldn't tie her own shoes. The woman in the fog didn't put on airs either or snub me with that *just putting up with her* eye roll that I used to get that made me feel as ashamed and ugly as an old bag lady. My heart shifted because of that, I think, and I sort of warmed up and started taking to her with what they used to call a Que Sera, Sera disposition. A real "whatever will be will be" state of mind. *Easygoing*—that says it all. And that made me want to be around her. And believe me, that's not like me. But it began to dawn on me that I felt *close* to the woman in the fog, like she was a true friend. A loyal friend. Somebody I could *trust*. That I can't explain, because as far as friends go, I trusted them about as far as I could throw them—there was nobody who could turn on a person faster than I could. I made darn sure I struck first before anybody got a chance to knock me down. *Knock me down? You damn sure better not be around when I get up.* But it wasn't like that with the woman in the fog. I cottoned to her despite myself.

Don't get me wrong, it wasn't any miracle. Miracles are what all you people want. But I've been studying things around here and made the deduction that miracles make good stories and that's about it. They're nothing like what they brag about or what you picture in your head. That was half my problem when I was alive—waiting for a miracle to happen so everything would be better. I've learned the hard way that you have to make your own miracles. And it takes a lot of time. And patience, which I never had much of.

So, warming up to the woman in the fog didn't happen all at once. First I had to use my common sense and figure out what she wanted from me. What was she going to twist my arm over? My whole life, I was set for a fight. I had to be. Everybody *always* wanted something from me. They were *always* trying to strong-arm me — do this, don't do that. Asking me for favors. Always expecting me to give, give, give when they never appreciated that I had to sweat blood for everything *I* ever got. So I waited for the woman in the fog to make her move. Take my word for it — the minute she showed her true colors, I was either going to cut and run or stand my ground and shake my fists. And slap her if I got mad enough.

But she didn't hassle me for anything. That was new. She didn't criticize me, either. To tell the truth, I got the impression that whatever I did, whatever I said, was okay with her. There was nothing in her eyes, nothing in the way she was standing that told me she was looking for trouble. Or interested in arguing with me. Or looking to pressure me into doing what I didn't want to do. That was pretty strange, because I'm accustomed to people trying to put the squeeze on me. And then me getting downright defiant and having a conniption fit or giving them the cold shoulder. She was just there, glowing in the fog. Peaches and cream. Soft as a 25-watt bulb. It made me think about the sun. It's just there. Take it or leave it, the sun still shines. She was more than a woman standing in the fog. She was a light in the dungeon.

101

Mary Patricia

I thought it was weird for me to describe the woman in the fog as a light in the dungeon. I had to stop and cogitate on that, because I never held an interest in dungeons. I was never one for fairytales or books about Robin Hood and the olden times when witches got tossed into them. But then, what I would call the features of a dungeon came to me: pitch black...cold...hopeless. My heart skipped a beat and my brain raced a million miles a minute from thinking about dungeons that way. I felt like the words "pitch black," "cold," and "hopeless" were *clues*, and that if I could iron them out, they would shed some light on things. I started to get really excited, because I could feel myself *learning*. It felt like lava pouring into the top of my head and firing up the tree of knowledge. *Bing. Bing. Bing.* Ever hear a slot machine hitting the jackpot? That's the sound I felt—*Bing. Bing. Bing.* Then I got afraid because my brain was flabbergasted, exploding with all this information that every last nerve in my dead body was dying to understand. I wanted to grab those words and thoughts in the worst way and keep them clenched in my fists before they disappeared and I lost everything.

That's when I reminded myself that I wasn't the old Pat anymore. I wasn't drowning. I didn't need to claw for air. Or fix the death grip on things I was terrified would slip through my fingers. I knew how to keep myself together now. I knew that if I kept myself calmed down, if I just let myself breathe and let the words *come to me* like they do in a book, I wouldn't chase away what I was dying to understand. And I'd have a chance to use my horse sense and cogitate. And unravel the clues. Contemplate what all this stuff meant...to me. That's when I started to *see the light*.

They talk about that a lot around here—"seeing the light"—but I never knew what they meant. I just figured all that rigamarole was for the smart people, people better than me. For the life of me, I never thought *seeing the light* would ever have anything to do with *me*. I had to let my brain settle down over that, because I was awful rattled. When I was alive, I always expected to be struck by lightning, or choke to death, or be thrown away in the garbage. In my whole life, I never expected anything good to happen to me. So, I couldn't hammer into my hard head that things were changing for the better for me. And that they had been for a while. Ever since coming over to this side, I expected to be stabbed with a pitchfork, and now here I was *seeing the light*. But not just seeing it, if that makes sense—feeling it...like it belonged to me. Like it was mine. Just like the sunlight. It doesn't just belong to the muckety-mucks. It's mine to sit in, too.

I had to stop ransacking my brain and just let my mind wander. So I deliberated about palm trees. And the Gulf of Mexico, and me and Jack watching the sun set over the water. All those bright colors. Orange. Red. Gold. Spreading across the horizon. Jack holding my hand. And the love I could feel coming from him right through his hand into mine. Into my heart. A gentle current of true love. I didn't think about it that way then. I sure wish I did. But I see it now. I see love, all its colors: orange...red... gold. Glowing. Bright. So much light. The woman in the fog—a golden, shining light in a miserable dungeon. Not a dungeon like in the movies. But something that *felt* like a dungeon. The dungeon in my heart. The dark place in my heart. The gloom—quicksand—I was stuck in during my life. A quicksand of unhappiness. Unhappiness that sucked the life out of me. Unhappiness that sucked me away from my life. The life I could have lived. Unhappiness holding me in misery at the bottom of a black pit, where I could hardly breathe. Depressed. All that depression in my heart. Smothering me. Clipping my wings. Crippling me. No sunshine in the quicksand. No stars. No light. All that gloom and misery in my heart stopping love from getting in. All that quicksand stopping me from seeing love. From feeling loved.

Daylight, *finally*. *Finally* I began to understand. I had words now, good words. I ingested them. I could see them in my head. And feel them in my body. Words that matched up with that heaviness inside my chest that never left me alone. *Gloom. Misery. Quicksand. Unhappiness. Depression.* Words I never admitted to, because I didn't understand that's what the heaviness was. Words I never even said to myself, because I didn't know they applied to me. The same words that got me so mad when anybody dared use them on me, like Kathleen when she complained that I seemed unhappy or depressed. They finally started to make sense. *Unhappy. Depressed.* Dictionary words carrying the same heaviness that I carried in my heart.

It started to register: the heaviness — *my* heaviness — was a *real* thing and it had a real name: *depression*. It was a real ailment. Just like the flu. Or cancer. It wasn't just bad moods. Or just Pat having a conniption fit. I wasn't just cranky. Or stubborn. Or selfish. Or just a bellyacher. I suffered from something real. Something with a name, a label: *depression*. And it disabled an awful lot of me.

For a good long time, I rolled those words around in my mind. It's like they'd been freed. Activated, or something. They were vibrating. Jumping. Happy for the chance to do their thing is how I'd describe it. Then I strung them together like a rope of excited pearls, making over how they glistened. I ran them through my imaginary fingers, feeling them, as silky as a tabletop after a nice waxing. A string of pearls. A string of words: *I was depressed I was unhappy. I suffered from depression. I suffered from the ailment of depression. Depression disabled an awful lot of me.* I lifted them over my head and slid them around my neck. A word necklace. Glowing words that fit me to a T. A glowing necklace that somehow touched my heart. That lit up my heart. That lifted it out of the gloom. Out of the quicksand.

I sat in the glow of those words — *pearls of wisdom*. I opened my heart all the way up and welcomed the light. Let it flood in. Let my spirits fly on wings I didn't know I had. I let the sunshine stay and warm my cold skin. I stood up and did a little tap dance in the glow of a moonbeam. I lay down under the millions of stars twinkling in the night sky. I was one of them.

I'd found what I'd been searching for my whole life: connection to my *real* self. And I had words now that told *the truth*.

102

Mary Patricia

She stood there, the woman in the fog did. Except the light surrounding her looked different. Clearer. Brighter, I'd have to say. So bright, in fact, that I could've used sunglasses. Sunnybrae Village Beach popped into my mind. The middle of August. Me on a blanket, basking in the sun, working on my tan. That's how bright the light was. It was like she was wearing it. Or generating it somehow. I could see every wrinkle in her burlap dress. Every crinkle around her eyes. Irish eyes. That's what they were. Green. Blue. Dark lashes. They sparkled in the light. I never met sparkling eyes before. Star eyes. They reflected light…at me. It made me think of a mirror. That's strange, isn't it? A mirror of light. I couldn't look away from her. It was like I was seeing her with brand-new eyes.

Her height surprised me. Even though she was the tallest woman I'd ever seen anywhere, even in the movies, she was a lot taller than I first thought. The funny thing is, I wasn't looking up at her. It's hard to explain. I was eyeball to eyeball with her, yet I was aware that she was much, much taller than me. I mean to say, I *knew* she was tall, but it didn't seem to matter. In plain English, I wasn't all gaga over her being so much bigger than me—maybe because I didn't feel small. It was a strange thing, me not comparing myself to her, to not be itching to level digs at her—you know, to knock her down a few pegs. For some reason, I didn't feel inferior to her. I wasn't scared of her, either. The biggest shock, though? I didn't have the urge to tear myself down. And no way José was that me. Not in a trillion years. "Hold your horses," I said to myself, "am I still *me?*" I had to take a minute to figure it out. Where was my old piss and vinegar? Where was the old Pat? Then I remembered. I wasn't the old Pat anymore. Things were going better for me now and I liked it that way. And no way José did I want to conjure up old times.

Here's where a cigarette would've been the icing on the cake in the relaxation department: me sitting back, taking long drags and trying for smoke rings while I was enjoying feeling so darn good and happy just *being*. Not having one trace of a spiteful frown on my face. And no urge to make one. No mean thoughts running around inside my head trying to bring me down. Just letting the woman in the fog *be* and not zinging her with snide remarks. Do you know how weird it was not feeling like I had a lead sinker tied around my neck? Not feeling sick to my stomach over how I didn't measure up? *Not* feeling like I had to kick and scream? I don't even remember a time when I didn't have my dukes up. It's like my heart had been untied and was allowed to just beat instead of battle. It tasted like freedom. *Freedom*—that's what it was. My whole life, I never knew what freedom tasted like.

I sat for a long time basking in my own sun.

103

Mary Patricia

I have to admit, I was taken aback by her antlers. It's not every day you see a giant woman with antlers. I'm at a loss for words for how to do them justice. It's hard to talk about if you've never seen such a thing. They were twisty and curly like tree branches, but I got the impression that they were as strong as bull horns. And they reached as far as the eye could see, far into the Milky Way. Reached up so high that all I could make out was light glowing in the distance. Like a halo. But different. Not like the wimpy yellow circle painted around Jesus' head on prayer cards. This light was no joke. Volts. Watts. Things like that. Coming from inside out. Emerging...that's a good word. Fluorescent? I'm trying to get the right words, but it's too hard to explain. Generated, I think. Like fire from rubbing two sticks together. Light generating from somewhere inside the antlers and glowing out, no different from a light bulb. Generated from inside her whole body maybe, like heat when you get to feeling so warm under your skin that you flush and that flush shows up on your cheeks and makes them red. Fever. No, hot flash—how does that grab you? That's the best I can do.

Here's the weird thing: the light had backbone. It's hard to explain. But I felt it. *It had soul.* Now, I'm not somebody who goes around using the word *soul*. It's too high and mighty for me. Too fake. It's for a homily at Mass. It never had any meaning to me, that word soul. As empty as a blank stare is what I would say. And real corncob outside of church, if you ask me. But *soul* fit. It flew right out of the dictionary and landed in my heart and described the light. Even linking it to the word *radiant*. Making me see how the light wasn't gaudy or make-believe—or corncob—like the lights from a circus or the haloes on Christmas cards. This was light with *meat*. Light with history behind it. *History*—that's a good word. The light was built by history. No, not exactly. It felt built *from*...a result of...

experience? Yes, that's the word...*experience*. That's the word that fits. Light built from...no, created from experience. Light created from experience. That's the ticket: *experience creates light*.

I floored myself with that...me, Mary Patricia, having those kinds of thoughts. Smart thoughts like a smart person—an educated person—would have. Those deductions should've been over my head, but they weren't. I understood what I was getting at. That's when even odder oddball things started to happen. Things I'll remember until the day I die. The only problem is that I'm already dead.

Words, hundreds maybe, came to me out of nowhere. Out-loud words. To-the-point words. Connect-the-dot words. It's like they tumbled out of the fog and crammed into my head and *made sense*. It was all I could do not to explode from awareness. That's a corny word, *awareness* is. Used by people who are always giving you advice. People with superiority complexes who like to lecture you about what you should do. But I don't have another word right now, so awareness will have to suffice. Let me put it this way: call it super awareness, figure on Superman with his X-ray vision. Mexican jumping bean awareness—caffeine injected straight into my brain—because I could've burst right out of my skin if it wasn't attached.

I got the shakes something terrible from being scared to death that I'd forget everything before I could write it all down. How else could I remember the words that were raining down on me like cats and dogs? But nobody writes anything down around here. It's all that mental telepathy stuff. And I needed a pencil and paper, damn it. Things I was used to. I couldn't let those words get away. *They had meaning.* They were keys to the castle...to *my* castle. Keys to *my home.* They were my *way* home. Sure as I knew my name, I knew I needed to soak up those words like a sponge. I needed to understand them—what they meant as far as I was concerned. Without getting the gist, I'd just go back to being the old Pat again. *I knew it.*

Panic started to choke me. Started clogging up my chest. Boiling my blood. And before I knew it, Ornery Pat burst in and started egging me on, goading me to pick a fight. Smack somebody. Smash something.

Tell everybody to go to hell. *I wanted to.* I was itching to get even for everything that was taken away from me.

That's when the fog, or something like it, settled over me and I remembered about calming down. I remembered that I could calm myself down. I knew how to do that now. So I said to myself, "Calm down. Calm down. Calm yourself down." I thought about smoking again—how exhaling always felt so good, so relaxing. When I exhaled a trail of smoke from deep inside my chest, all was right with the world. It felt that good. So, I took the hint and that's what I did—exhaled, only without the smoke. And I used helpful words. Upbeat thinking. That kind of stuff to get away from Ornery Pat: *Don't get your bowels all in an uproar or you'll chase every single keyword away.* If I stay calm, the keywords won't go anywhere, because they belong to me. They are mine. They're mine because I've listened. I've cogitated. I've learned. The keywords are mine because *I earned them.* Nobody can take them away from me. It's not possible because *I have the control.* It's all up to me. *Calm down. Calm down.*

I did. I calmed down. And I felt really good about myself.

104

Mary Patricia

I let the words sift through me. They reminded me of snowflakes. You know how each one is different? Some were broken to bits. Some fell into a formation and read similar to poetry. But not just any poetry: *my* poetry, if you get my drift. My words but polished, lifted like they had a glow to them. I was never a poet when I was alive, so I'm half embarrassed to admit that sometimes I tried to write poems. I was always so ashamed of that, afraid someone would catch me there with my pants down and let the cat out of the bag. And I'd be a laughingstock. Made fun of like I was a retard. Called a dingbat for thinking I might have a shot at putting nice words and pretty thoughts together. Who was I to put rhyming words on paper? I had no call to. No education. Poetry writing was for Princeton people. Not for me, a stupid woman who didn't even finish high school. Who was only fit to be a pig farmer, according to how my teachers put it. I never learned anything about poetry outside of "Jack and Jill." Half the time the words didn't make sense the way they were put together. But half the time they did, and I got the picture. One time Kathleen asked me about a poem she had to learn for school. I remember she didn't understand it. It didn't even rhyme, but the meaning just flowed into my brain and I understood it anyhow. And I helped her. I explained it to her. I felt good about that.

I've always had bits and pieces of words floating around in the dark inside me. It drove me off my rocker—letters and words right on the tip of my tongue but always out of reach. I drove myself nuts trying to grab hold of them. In the worst way, I wanted to pull them all together and use them for deep thoughts and quick wit, but I never could. It made me feel so stupid having words rattle around inside me like broken bones, yet not having anything to say. So, it wasn't easy for me to really believe that things had changed for me for the better. That I'd changed for the better.

Thinking about it, though, made me see that I had. Because I was sick of calling myself stupid and crazy. Fed up with acting dumb. I was a learner now, a student, and I was learning to give myself credit for getting the hang of things. For being correct.

Remember the scarecrow in *The Wizard of Oz*? How he thought he didn't have a brain? And how it turned out that he was a brain but what he lacked was some fancy degree? I cogitated on that poor scarecrow. How he was smart the whole time but didn't know it. Then it occurred to me that thinking you don't have a brain proves that you do have a brain or you wouldn't be able to cogitate on not having one. That angle sat right with me. It went against common sense, me thinking that I didn't have a brain or that the one I had didn't work. I finally came to the deduction that yes, *I had brain and yes, it worked*. I was the only one who would never believe it.

Figuring out that I had something going on upstairs was a big deal for me. Even though I could hardly believe it was true, I concluded it was high time to jump in with both feet and take it as fact. I was done fighting air. Though I have to say, Ornery Pat begged to differ. She started rearing up, trying to cuss her way into my head. The only way I could get rid of her was to chase her away with my cigarette breathing. A hundred times, maybe two hundred, I inhaled and exhaled, repeating to myself over and over, *I am a good person! I am a good person!* If I could have, I would've burned that sentence into my brain with a branding iron so I'd never forget it. So Ornery Pat would get the message and leave me alone—I was so sick and tired of her.

105

Mary Patricia

I've never been what you would call a bleeding heart, but I'd noticed that changing, too. The best I can describe it is that it felt like warm wings were hugging me, warming up my blood. Making me feel what I would call *kindhearted*. Or *openhearted*. Like how you'd feel toward a baby bird. I think it was due to the woman in the fog and me taking to her. She was always with me—that part I'd figured out. I don't know why she didn't have better things to do, and I didn't ask. But I was glad for her company. She seemed polite, if you know what I mean...nice. She didn't put on airs. Plus, she understood my lingo. And I was starting to understand hers, though I wouldn't exactly call her a chatterbox.

I kind of wished I could talk things over with her, because I had concerns: I was worried over Ornery Pat. I have to say I was more than worried: I was sick-to-my-stomach, upset that Ornery Pat might ruin everything for me with her conniption fits. That she'd start bitching and bellyaching and smash everything to hell like she always did.

I didn't know what to do. What to think. I was so mixed-up and scared stiff of Ornery Pat coming back and living inside my head again. There wasn't anybody around to give me their two cents. Except for the woman in the fog. So I just looked at her, feeling like a wet puppy dog begging for a bone. *Defeated*—that's the word I'm looking for. *What's the use?* That was my mindset. No matter what I did, Ornery Pat was always going to come back with her rage. Nobody could do anything about that fact. Not even the woman in the fog.

So why was I bothering with her? She was probably just a figment of my imagination anyhow. Even if she was real, she wouldn't be able to sympathize with me—with what it was like to live inside somebody who wasn't *you* and not be able to get out. To have a stranger—a foreigner—wear your body and control the show. How could I put that in plain English? Who even had the smarts to get *that* picture? How could I tell about how the real me had been locked away since...since those nights in the sweaty bed with my stinking sister, Bobby? How could I point out that *Pat was an actor?* A character walking around on a stage? A woman I didn't know? A woman I hated? The shadow I wanted to get rid of, but never would? It was too much. I wanted to collapse into a puddle right then and there.

But just when I was ready to cave in, images started floating across my mind no different from puffy white clouds drifting across a blue sky on a windy day. Salt water. Waves in the ocean. The Gulf of Mexico. Spring—green leaves budding out on tree branches. How it always made me feel so...so content. I'd forgotten all about spring from living in Florida for so long. Mount Rushmore, of all things.

Laying eyes on Mount Rushmore for the first time and thinking back to the shockwaves that practically rattled my teeth from seeing it. It boggled my mind. I'd never in my entire life seen anything so big, so enormous. It was out of this world. I remember how...this is a strange thing to say...I felt big inside my body from it. Like I wasn't separate from it. Like I was part of that mountain and it was part of me, but I'd forgotten about that sensation until I saw the image again.

I remember shushing my mind for thinking all that stuff about Mount Rushmore, saying, "Pat, you've really gone bananas this time." Calling myself stupid. Dumb. But I couldn't shake the sensation of how its bigness felt like it *belonged* to me. How its hugeness swelled inside me, fitting me to a T. Filling in all the spaces. I remember I couldn't stop staring at those carved faces—don't ask me whose they were up there on the side of that mountain, because I couldn't even tell you. All I can say is that inside I felt this...this...this power, like an engine revving. More than vim and vigor. Vim and vigor plus *nerve.* Do you know what I mean by *nerve?* I felt like I was *somebody,* and I knew it. Inside, I just *knew* I was somebody. Somebody strong. Somebody who had *muscles.* I was shaking like a leaf, too. Not with anger like I'm used to, but shaking with satisfaction. A real, raring-to-go kind of feeling that really hit the spot. Like all was right with the world. *All was right with me.* I'd never felt a sensation like that before —

excited and strong and contented all rolled into one. And I never ever expected to feel anything like it again.

That's where I was wrong. *It was back.* That feeling of bigness inside. Huge. Huge. Swelling out my insides. Filling up all the empty spaces. Revving up my heart, making me feel like it was beating inside a mountain of strength. I had to ask myself then: if my heart felt like it was beating inside a mountain of strength, and it was beating inside *me*, and there was no Mount Rushmore or anything like it in sight to get me overexcited, then *I had to be* that mountain of strength, right? Me. Mary Patricia. A mountain of strength.

That's when I collapsed. But not for the worst. I collapsed from being thrilled. From pure, unadulterated happiness. I collapsed, but I collapsed *up*. I know it doesn't make sense to you, but that's how it was. I was floating. And flying. Like the last chain had been sawed off my ankle and I was freed. Wait a minute... Telling you all this, I'm seeing now that *I* didn't collapse, did I? *It was Ornery Pat that collapsed.* Ornery Pat collapsing and falling away. Ornery Pat letting me go. No...that's not exactly it. There's something else. Let me think. Let me get this right: Ornery Pat didn't let me go. *I* let *her* go. *I let Ornery Pat go.* That's why I was flying so free.

Oh, for pity's sake. It's finally sinking in.

106

Mary Patricia

All this is really throwing me for a loop. It feels like there's no space between what's happened before and what's happening now. I can't explain it, but everything is *here*. Not as a story after the fact, but as I'm living it right now. It feels weird. I'm seeing things. But I'm doing them at the same time. There's no distance between then and now. Here and there. I'm outside myself while I'm inside myself. And I'm aware of it all. I'm living and watching at the same time. Doing. Observing. *Learning.* Telling you. All this stuff at once. Like giving a blow-by-blow report from the battlefield. Like on the news. It just struck me—*forget about Heaven*. It's nothing, nothing like they said. Nothing... If I'd only known. If I'd only known...

Oh, I'd give my eye teeth for a real cigarette and a strong cup of black coffee and a place to sit and cogitate all these things that are pouring into my head like rays of bright sunshine. *I see my kitchen on Mark Twain Drive.* It's lighting up my mind like a shooting star.

Now I'm back there. Only it's not there—it's here, right now. Ruffled curtains starched and ironed like I just hung them up. Chock full o'Nuts—that heavenly coffee—percolating. I hear the *blub-blub. Blub-blub.* Let me close my eyes for a just a second. Let me just stand still and take it all in. Nothing in this world smells better than coffee brewing in a pot. *I am home.* I am home.

I can't believe it. I look down. A half pack of Raleighs sits on my old kitchen table, a lit one in my favorite ceramic ashtray with the chips and nicotine stains. I reach for it. My hand is shaking. But I get it to my lips and inhale. *It's a real cigarette.* I inhale long and deep. And hold the smoke in my lungs. Hold it. Hold it. The burn hurts so good. *This is heaven. This is heaven.* I blow out a thick, white stream and watch it curl and disappear in the air. *This is real.*

I stroll over to the stove and pour steaming coffee into my favorite mug, the one that names me "World's Best Mother." I sit back down at the table, run my fingers over the smooth Formica, take another drag from my cigarette, sip the most delicious cup of coffee I have ever had, and stare out the window just like in the old days. But outside the light is odd, different from when I lived in this house on this street so many, many years ago. It's…what's the word I'm looking for? *Diffused*. That's it, the light is diffused. More like a glow…an afterglow, I guess you would say. What's left after a thunderstorm. Pale yellow. Soft. Everything outside is blurred into this light. I take another drag. Another swallow… My brain unlocks.

I've had my gripes about this side. Coffee and cigarettes were high on my list. I figured that after a lifetime of aggravation, God the Father, His Son, or one of the hundreds of saints I've "adored" or the souls in purgatory I beseeched over the years could've taken pity on me when I came over and at least thrown a few stubbed-out butts and some stale decaf my way. But that's not the way it is. And I suppose it's not the way it ever was. Nothing's easy around here. I'm still mad that this isn't the heaven they taught me about—the one I was promised— when I was alive. It's taken me a long time to come to grips with the way things really work. I came here expecting life to be a piece of cake. After all, I made novenas. I made sacrifices. Never missed Mass even on holy days of obligation. I thought I earned Heaven a thousand times over. Boy, was I in for a rude awakening. You think it's tough where you are? That's nothing. Things are a thousand times tougher on this side. Especially for someone who doesn't know the ropes.

I was sold a bill of goods, that's for sure. When I was on your side, I never had a problem getting people to do things for me. I could always persuade some handsome buck to help me with my suitcase when I was flying north for a vacation. Or rile my kids up enough to get them to drop what they were doing and come running. Around here? Forget about anybody waiting on you. Believe me, I can attest to that. There's no use in begging for favors, either. Or crying the blues when you don't get what you want. Take it from me, it's just a big waste of energy. Around here, everybody's got important things to do, and listening to you whine and carry on isn't one of them. Still, that didn't stop me from griping that they could at least offer a few services to people like me who were sick and tired of it all and just couldn't do things for themselves. For pity's sake, even in Florida you can call up and order groceries and they'll deliver them right to your door. And for a nice tip, they'll put them away for you, too. The way I looked at it, it wouldn't have killed them to help an old lady out. But that's not the way it is in this so-called heaven. If you want something, you have to do it for yourself. It's not the way I'd run things, but nobody asked me.

What's big around here is the word *create*. I swear, if I heard that word once, I heard it a million times. I heard it so many times that I wanted to spit. But my attitude didn't change a thing. *Create*—that's the main idea in this place. And believe me, you can't avoid it. Whatever you want, you have to *create* it for yourself. It's dog-hard work, and *you* have to do it. They call it aligning yourself with specific conditions to create your soul's desire. Sounded like gobbledygook. A corny line from a Disney movie. Take it from somebody who knows: this business of creating for yourself is no picnic. It's too hard. And I was too tired.

That's why I decided to get back at them and their dumb ideas. So I played dead—dead-as-a-doornail dead. Trust me, playing dead doesn't get you anywhere. It doesn't even get you any sympathy. I should've listened to the grapevine on that one. Because unlike my kids, nobody came running. If you play dead, everybody assumes you are and leaves you be until you decide to get up and live again. That was a tough lesson. It took me a while to come to the conclusion that I could play dead for all eternity if I wanted and nobody would try to coax me out of it. I could've been lying there in the dirt, cursing all the action going on around me and holding on to being pissed about not having coffee and cigarettes, and nobody would bat an eye. I didn't understand why having a temper tantrum didn't work—where I came from, everybody would've been hell-bent for election to help me. Live and learn, that's what I used to say. Die and learn, that's my new motto. I must be doing okay, because here I am right now relaxing in my kitchen in a home I love, smoking a *real* cigarette and drinking *real* coffee.

Though I'll tell you, it's not the 1960s anymore—I'm aware of that. I don't need it to be. I don't need to go back to then when I'm enjoying now—enjoying soaking up feeling so good about sitting here at my table and staring outside into that soft, golden glow. It's like I'm in a gentle bubble that I hope never bursts.

The woman in the fog is with me. I can sense her. I look over to my right. She's sitting there at the end of the table smoking, too. I'm so happy that she's not carping at me, bearing down on me with criticism and disgust. I like this friendship. It's easy. I feel wanted.

We both exhale at the same time. I watch smoke ribbons drift around the room, and I'm loving, *loving* the smell of lit cigarettes. I look over at her and smile. She nods and smiles back at me. I know it's time to ask the question.

107

Mary Patricia

A big swallow of coffee. Another long drag of my Raleigh. Exhale. Stub out the cigarette. Take a deep breath. Find the nerve. Find the nerve. Finally I put it to her. *What about Ornery Pat?* I don't speak the words out loud. I say them in my mind and direct them to the woman in the fog, staring straight into her eyes. She looks at me and blinks, and instantly I am peering into Ornery Pat's eyes. I have to catch my breath, because they are vacant, spiritless eyes. They look naked and scared. *I need to run.* Run faster than I have ever run in my entire life. Run like my hair's on fire. Run like I'm being chased by the devil waving a butcher knife.

I have to catch my breath. I have to breathe. I know how to do this now. I don't have to run. I can calm myself down. I've learned how to do that. I'm a learner now. A student. I have a brain. It works. I've proven that to myself. Calm down. Calm down.

I light another Raleigh and take a hard drag and pull smoke so far into my lungs I think it will touch my knees. My eyes feel like sandpaper. I blink, hoping I'm just hallucinating. That this is all a bad dream and I'll wake up in my bed in Florida and be able to stumble out to the liquor cabinet for a shot of vodka to numb this bleeding grief. But this is not make-believe. Or a figment of my imagination. This is as real as anything I ever went through before I died.

Ornery Pat is here—I know this with every tingling nerve in my body—and she's looking at me through the kind eyes of the woman in the fog. Dead hearts beat, and mine is racing. I settle back in the chair and stare out the window again. The scent of coffee wraps around me like one of my hand-stitched quilts. The kitchen echoes with long-gone laughing times and I feel that old sense of happiness creeping into my heart. I am so glad for the coffee and cigarettes and a nice person to share them with. I know I'm home. *I know I'm safe.*

I look again into Ornery Pat's eyes. Her living story starts unfolding right in front of me. I see her anger—as red as flames—erupting, spitting blazing cinders. Her anger—a display of rapid gunfire against a night sky. I can't handle this. Her anger is too much. There's no reining it in. It's too tremendous. I don't even have words to describe it. It's tying my stomach up in knots. My head is pounding. All I want to do is look away. *I will do this; I will do this,* I keep telling myself.

But I'm not so sure I can. Ornery Pat's anger is a current of wild electricity zapping and buzzing me. Ramming against me like waves at high tide. I brace my feet on the floor and don't take my eyes off her. Her rage is scorching me. It's a wild fire. I'm afraid she'll burn me to death like a witch at the stake and we'll both be done for. I'm a hairsbreadth away from screaming UNCLE. Positive that any second I'm going to burst into flames. And nothing will be left of me except ashes.

Wait. Hold your horses. *Something's there.* I know it! *Something's there!* I stop staring into the flames of Ornery Pat's anger and lean forward into its heat. It singes my eyebrows. Her fury is a wall of fire. A three-alarm blaze. I squint hard and catch sight of something— *tiny gaps.* There! There! Between the flames! *Between the flames,* I shout to myself. *Look between the flames.*

There they are: *breaks.* Tiny spaces. So small they're hardly detectable. But something's there, *I know it!* Sure as shooting, I know it. But how do I know? What if this is just a flash-in-the-pan illusion? A false impression? My eyes playing tricks on me? After all, I am dead. How do I know anything at all is real? What the hell can I believe? *Myself?* I take another drag off my cigarette. Then another. One more for good luck. *Yes,* I decide, I can take up for myself. I can believe myself. I can be on my own side. I want to be on my own side. *I saw what I saw.* I know I was looking at *something.* Something is there.

How do I figure this out? What do I do? *Words.* I need a list of words. I'll start with the alphabet. A...b...c...d... I run through the letters twice. On the third time around, I hesitate at the letter C. C...*cold.* The word washes goose bumps over me. Chills. Cold chills. The sense of never feeling warm. Never feeling protected. I allow myself to sink into this sense of bitter cold. It is a pit of isolation. Of despair. I am an abandoned body. Twitching in the dark. It's unnerving me. This is the center of cold-blooded torment, and I'm here in it. Freezing fingers grab at me. Thick, freezing fingers. This is despair. I recognize it. It's grabbing at my arms and legs. Yanking fistfuls of my skin and hair. It's robbing me of my life. This...this anguish. So cold. So icy. Thick. Clotted. Muddy quicksand. It's sucking me under...under into its damp, sunken grave. I'm a prisoner. I toss and turn, fling myself around. Shriek like a banshee. But I'm buried inside a tomb inside my own body. I'm suffocating. I'm drowning. Despair is exterminating me. I am losing all hope. I have no fight left. I am disappearing.

Suddenly a flash. And a fireball. Flames exploding all the way up from my groin. An eruption of blistering fire. A capable fire. A cremating fire. A protecting fire. *A rescuing fire.*

I fall back against my chair, too exhausted to lift my cigarette or take a sip of lukewarm coffee. How is it that a woman can ever know what is hiding? How can a living woman know about frozen, invisible things? Things that bleed without blood? That cause third-degree burns but leave no blisters? All I can do is stare into space. *Stunned*—that's the only word I can conjure up right now, and it is way too small, but it will have to do. I am *stunned* beyond belief at the intensity of Ornery Pat's anger. *It is severe,* I'll tell you that. It's an incinerator. In the blink of an eye, it'll burn anything to a crisp—*anything*. And the *extent* of it. Hysterical. Unending. Perpetual, that's what it is. Perpetual rage. Oh my God, a ton of bricks just hit me: Ornery Pat's rage is *my* rage.

I straighten up in my chair and light another cigarette. I have to cogitate on this. I walk over to the stove and pour fresh coffee into my mug and go over to the window and run my fingers down the curtains. They're pale pink—mauve, I guess you'd say—with ruffles. I've always loved the look of starched and ironed curtains hanging at a window. Nice and homey. Just touching them touches my heart. I can't explain it, but they're "home" to me. A place where I belong. A place to take off my shoes. A place where *I am.* I am safe here. I can feel my heart speaking to me. I can hear it.

It's safe to look, my heart tells me. *It's safe to see.*

108

Mary Patricia

The glow outside my window boggles my mind. *Luminescent.* That's the best description I can come up with — *a luminescent glow.* But words don't do it justice. It's the best part of light and music. It moves your heart. The way sunlight does when it breaks through the clouds after a hurricane. Or listening to Patti Page croon "Tennessee Waltz" — that song always brought tears to my eyes. Just having the chance to see such a golden sight melts your heart into the feeling of secret joy that you'd be embarrassed to admit because it's so personal. It looks like love. It *feels* like love. It gives you a lump in your throat. It lifts your spirits. I feel my insides smiling. Making me think I can do anything.

I've been moved to tears — to feeling love — a million times when I was alive. But the good feelings never lasted. "Tennessee Waltz" always ended. And hurricanes constantly threatened. And the soft feelings in my heart faded away like snowflakes on a Florida sidewalk. You'd try to get them back, but they were gone until the next time. But you never knew when the next time would be. Or if you'd ever feel that way again for all the troubles in your life. Love and joy didn't belong to me. That's what I thought. I didn't deserve any of that good stuff. I'd try to grab hold of happiness, but it flew right out of my fingers. It came and went with the wind.

But this luminescent glow...the sensation of it, the *ahh, deepness* of it...is different. It's like...how can I explain this? It's not flighty or shallow. It's not makeup slapped on your face to hide wrinkles. Or something that swings with a mood. It's a *thing. A rooted thing.* A structure. Even though it's a glow, it's something developed, built. From the ground up and the heart out. That's what I see. It's something solid. But not solid like concrete. No way is it rigid. Solid in the way of reliable. Dependable. Always there. *I can feel it.* It's a solid presence, but fluid. It's like the softest water in the world, but it doesn't get you wet. It embraces you. And...how about that? It expands. I see it expanding in waves and ripples. Flowing. Widening. Unfolding like a beautiful rose. Except the rose is light flaring outward. And upward. It's…it's nature. It's alive. *I can sense it breathing.* It's…it's…how do I say this? It has a real spirit. It's life, that's what it is. It has a pulse. *I* have a pulse. I'm seeing that this isn't so weird considering all the living things everywhere. Plants. Trees. People. Wind. I'll add lipstick to that list, because there's nothing more alive than a Revlon red.

Now listen to this: the glow breathes. I breathe the glow. No different from breathing in the sunlight. Or inhaling every word of "Tennessee Waltz" when it comes on the radio. *Everything* shares the same space; that's what I'm getting. I thought I was separate, but I'm not. Nothing is. I never understood that. *It* is all one. I'm part of *it*. And *it* is part of me. Everything is connected. It didn't make sense before. But all the pieces are falling together for me. I can feel it plugging in…the lamp cord connecting to the outlet. I'm starting to trust it. Like the woman in the fog. I feel myself inviting myself to stretch my arms out into the light. I feel myself starting to welcome it. I feel like I'm tip-toeing toward the light. I want to embrace it. I want it to embrace me.

I do what I thought I'd never do in a zillion years. I sink recklessly into the glow's warmth. I'm not all in—not yet. I keep one foot outside, just in case. For protection. In case I have to run. Well, as long as I'm here, I may as well enjoy it. I allow it to ease my tension. Weird that you don't realize how tense you are until your muscles begin to unwind and your body starts feeling as free as a floating feather. This is taking a warm bath without the water. I feel peaceful. Gentle-hearted toward myself. But stable. Open, even. Receptive. That's the word…receptive. This isn't an attitude. This is me. This is my heart lifted of sorrow. This is me without all the black clouds. *This is really me.* The me out from under everything that was smothering me. Drowning me.

I glow. The true me glows. I might as well pull my other leg in.

109

Mary Patricia

I mosey back over to my kitchen chair. It's yellow vinyl, straight out of the '50s. We brought the whole set—table and chairs—with us when we moved here from our other house. It wore like iron. We had plenty of good times around this table. Penny-ante poker games. A lot of singing "Happy Birthday." I'll tell you one thing: my kitchen was always spotless. Up until the day Jack and I moved out of this house, you couldn't find a crumb anywhere—not even with a magnifying glass. I was proud of that.

I'm just coming to think now that love lived here. Not that living here was perfect. We had our terrible troubles. But the house, it had this feel… A really good feel. I loved this house. I never thought in a thousand million years that I'd ever have a chance to come back here. I never thought in a thousand million years that I'd be able to learn what I call highfalutin things, either. That was about as far-fetched as me going to the moon. Here I am, though, sitting on top of my own learning. I was always below, if you get my drift. I waited for other people to dig me out. For other people to do the work of learning the hard stuff and then just telling me what to do. But taking orders never did sit right with me. Boy, that really raised my hackles. I guess that's when Ornery Pat took over.

I'm hem-hawing. Of this, believe me, I am aware. I have my reasons. Such as I don't want to look too close at what I saw in Ornery Pat's anger. That's a funny thing, don't you think? Because I have a pretty good handle on the "whys." That fire-breathing, hate-the-world fury all started with that good-for-nothing dog-faced sister, Bobby. It's not the "whys" making me drag my feet. It's those gaps I noticed situated between the flames of Ornery Pat's anger that are getting to me. I'm sensing a world of hurt hovering around and I don't like it. But there comes a time, I suppose… A time not to look away. A time to face things. The old me would run. But the new me…Mary Patricia… I…I have this nagging feeling that looking at what I don't want to see is going to *help* me.

But *help* isn't the right word. The idea of *help* aggravates me. Reminds me of fingernails scraping down a blackboard. I can feel Ornery Pat bristling right now. Anyhow, what do I need *help* for? Help sounds like something somebody else decides you need even though you never asked for it. Help sounds like pity. Like some do-gooder riding into your life deciding to "help" you get your act together.

Who the hell do they think they are, anyway? I damn sure never asked for their "help." I'm doing just fine without it, and I sure as hell don't want their pity or their two cents, Ornery Pat gripes in my ear.

I don't need a crystal ball to predict Ornery Pat rising to the bait and going off half-cocked over an insult that infuriates the tar out of her. Pulling the bite-off-her-nose-to-spite-her-face trick and flinging all my hard work into the flames.

I have to calm myself down. Figure this out. *Breathe, Mary Patricia. Breathe. Relax. Just relax.* But it really ticks me off, because help is the wrong idea. I don't want *help*. I don't need *help*. Okay. Okay. All right, already. So, *help* doesn't hit the mark. I don't have to get my bowels in an uproar over it. I am allowed to decide for myself that it's off the track. I don't have to fall for the wrong word. Or make it fit when it doesn't just because it's there and it's easier. Or because "somebody" says *help* is what I need.

I have power now. I can make my own decisions. Decide what I want. Decide what to think. I don't need anybody else's opinion. I don't want anybody else's opinion—I want my own. I want to find the right word. A word that hits the spot. That says the truth about what this nagging, uncomfortable feeling is. And what it means. What it's saying. Because if I needed *help*, I'd ask for it. If looking at what I don't want to see will only give me help I don't want, then why bother? What's the big payoff for me? I'm not looking for anything. I'm perfectly contented sitting here in my kitchen, drinking my coffee and smoking my cigarettes with my friend, the woman in the fog.

110

Mary Patricia

Speaking of the woman in the fog, I feel her staring at me. Not in a dirty-look way. Maybe how you'd look at somebody you really loved. How the look has really special meaning — really deep feelings, I'd say. Her looking at me doesn't bother me. In fact, I feel relaxed. *Safe* is a good word. *Safe* isn't a word I'm accustomed to using, but it fits. Though I've been around here long enough to know when something's up. And I'd just as leave ignore her. But I can't. But I don't want to look into her eyes again, either, because no doubt I'll spot Ornery Pat there and I'll have to go through all that rigamarole again and I'll be right back where I started, not wanting to look at what I don't want to see.

I smoke another Raleigh all the way down to its filter. If good manners weren't my concern, I'd lick the last few drops of coffee out of the mug. I'm sidetracking myself. Fiddling around. But it isn't working. There's something... something there... *I feel it.* Something is pressing on my heart. Squeezing my lungs. It's this drive...this push...this...*pull*...to deal with *something*. Like I'm dying of thirst and my whole body is tingling, absolutely positively sure that there's an oasis close by if I'd just drag myself to it. I can *feel* water in the air. But I can't see it. The water I don't see is a ghost whispering to me. Urging me forward. Calling me closer. *Something* super-duper is calling me to look at what I don't want to see. Pulling me toward the "water" that will quench my thirst. I sense this, but it doesn't make sense, if you know what I mean.

I'm so confused. I don't understand how looking at what I don't want to see has anything to do with anything good. I can't lie: I felt empty inside most of my life. I've always ignored it, figuring it wasn't real. That it was just my imagination. Or I was just cranky. Or it had something to do with me being feebleminded. Or always doing things the wrong way. That empty feeling in my heart never left for very long. No matter what, it always came back. I mean, do tell, I'm dead and it's still alive. That must mean that it wasn't only in my head. Especially since the head I had when I was alive isn't the same kind of head I have now. Whatever it is seems to have followed me here. So that has to mean that whatever is bothering me is *real*. If it's real—like the flu or cancer or the chickenpox—then maybe something can be done about it. That's the only deduction that makes sense. This needs cogitating.

I must say the woman in the fog is very patient. She must have all the time in the world. Which I guess she does. Which makes me think that I do, too. So I give a big sigh and just sit back and enjoy the glow out the window. And let the daydreams come. This is the good part. My bones feel like jelly. And I feel as if I'm melting. No cares. No worries.

Hey, how about that...as easy as pie, the word intuition floats up and it's levitating right in front of my eyes. Sparkling letters dancing on a cloud. You can't see me smiling. But I am. Really big. *Intuition*—that's the ticket. Why didn't I think of it before? *Intuition*. It's a perfect dictionary word. It says it all. It's raining over me like stardust from a fairy godmother's wand. *Intuition*. I can't get over it. That's what I've been feeling—*my intuition. Women's intuition,* they always called it. Having eyes in the back of your head. I used to have it for my kids. I could tell what they were doing when my back was turned. I never knew that intuition was *really real*. I never expected *women's intuition* to be more than just a joke to make my kids mind.

Figuring this out makes me think that I should be happy as a clam. Why aren't I then? Why is that emptiness gnawing at my gut? Slicing me open? I feel as if I'm falling apart. I'm such a dum-dum. I should've picked this answer up quicker. *Intuition*. It was as clear as the nose on my face. *It was biting the nose on my face,* for pity's sake. Now Ornery Pat's here again, kicking the back of my head, giving me a headache. I can't let her take over. *Take a deep breath,* I warn myself. I do. Then another. I remind myself again and again that I don't put myself down anymore. Ornery Pat is not the boss around here.

Give yourself a break, Mary Patricia. I say this about a hundred times.

I think about nice things. Things that are important to me, to Mary Patricia. Dictionary words. Learning. Feeling warm. Feeling safe. Feeling like a good person. Thinking that I have a brain that works good.

111

Mary Patricia

Right in front of me like I'm watching a show on television, I see a little girl. She's about one or two. Sitting on the floor in a white cotton dress with a ruffled hem. Legs straight out in front of her. She's got on baby shoes—tan hightops, they look like. Her mother is sitting on her knees facing the little girl, tying her shoes. Clear as day, I hear the mother say *shoe*. She looks at the little girl, says the word, and points to a shoe. This goes on for a long time—the mother pointing to the shoe, then repeating the word *shoe*.

I watch the little girl. The look on her face. It's as bright as sunlight. I *see* the wheels going around in her head. I *see* her learning. Somehow, some way, that baby *knows* that this is very important. She's excited. Almost giggling. She's realizing that there's a certain sound for that thing on her foot her mother is pointing to. That it's a *special* thing. It's a *shoe*. And it has its very own sound...*shhh ooo...shoe*. And it's very different from the jumble of all the other things and sounds around her. When the mother says, "Point to your shoe," *the little girl does!* It feels like a celebration. I want to clap for them. Both the mother and the little girl are laughing. She's done it! The little girl has connected the dots from her mother's word and pointing finger to her shoe. It makes sense to her. I can see that something clicked in her brain—the plug went in the outlet—and now she has...she has...

What does she have? I keep asking myself that. What does the little girl have? What's the word for what she has now? Oh good grief, the word *power* just flew into my mind like a speeding bullet. *Power. Power*—that can't be right. I want to shoo that word away like a gnat, because it sounds ridiculous. A baby with power? What kind of power can a baby have? But then I remember that old saw: *knowledge is power*. I never got that. But looking at that little girl makes me think that there really is power—yes, *power*—in knowledge.

How confusing. And weird to think that the word *power* can really have anything to do with knowledge. Can that be right? I mean, *really right?* That there's some other kind of real power besides the kind of power that I'm used to—lifting barbells kind of power, for instance? Or the long-arm-of-the-law kind of power? Or the almighty power of God? That's the kind of power that I'm accustomed to—the kind that can beat you up. The kind that can do you in.

This is all news to me—a type of power that lights you up from the inside, like with that little girl. My heart is doing flip-flops, that's for sure. I never found a treasure, but I think this is probably what it feels like when you know you're getting close to the gold…really, really jittery, I'd say. I'm on to something. Only what? What's the word I'm looking for to describe exactly what *it* is that I'm on to? Okay. I'm going to concentrate and figure this out.

I surmise that the kind of power in that little girl *is* knowledge power. After all, it stands to reason. She's not big enough to build muscles with weights. So it's not physical power she's all gaga about. And since she's not fighting and winning her way through the world with a badge on her chest and a pair of six-shooters strapped to her hip like Marshal Matt Dillon in "Gunsmoke" with the sharp behind, it isn't the power of law shining in her eyes. And she's too little to clobber anybody over the head with the Ten Commandments and a list of mortal sins to go with them, so it can't be the power of God filling her up with joy. Still, she has a certain power—that much is obvious to me now. I see it, but I don't understand it. I'm stuck, because I think there's something else going on along with that power of hers…something besides just knowledge. It's like her learning—her found knowledge, so to speak—comes with something else. Some kind of prize, I'd say. A halo, maybe? It has to be *something*, because my intuition tells me that there's more to this whole thing than her just learning the word *shoe*. What is it? *What is it?*

Okay. Let's see. Muscles give you strength to pound the tar out of somebody. A badge and a gun give you license to shoot first and ask questions later. God puts the fear of death and the hope of heaven in you. But knowledge…what does knowledge give you besides understanding? I don't get it. And I'm about ready to tear my hair out.

I glance over at the woman in the fog. I wish she'd help me out. But she doesn't say a word—not one word. She just sits there looking at me with a sparkle in her eye that reminds me of diamonds. Funny…that takes me back to the engagement ring Jack got for me more years ago than I can count. It only had one tiny diamond, but it meant the world to me. I never doubted Jack's love for me, not once. I didn't understand why, but he had faith in me, too. *He believed in me.* Talk about feeling good. It's a tremendous feeling having somebody believe in you that much.

I glance at the woman in fog again. I'll be darned. *She* has faith in me. *That's what the sparkle in her eyes is telling me.* She thinks I have what it takes to come up with the right answer about this knowledge business. I can see it by the way she's looking at me. Too bad. I hate to be the bearer of bad news, but her confidence in me is dearly misplaced. Anyway, to my way of thinking, if she would just clear this up for me once and for all, I could relax and enjoy myself and we could smoke a few more cigarettes in peace.

Oh good grief! That's it, isn't it? That's the word I'm looking for… *confidence.* That's the word for the special glow in that little girl. It wasn't just her learning about the shoe. It's how she *felt* about herself by learning about her shoe. *Confidence*—that's her reward. Her prize. That's the light in her eyes. The light of confidence shining through. Oh good grief, *I called it right!* I didn't even know that when I talked about the halo, I was talking about a glow, a light. How about that? I can't get over it.

This must be magic. I never deduced things such as this. *How about that?* I must know more than I give myself credit for. Maybe there really is something to this whole idea of intuition. To knowing something long before your brain catches up. I'm flabbergasted…bowled over…that I deduced something like this. I can hardly explain how good I feel for "knowing" about the halo before I put all the pieces together in my head. Saying *halo* out of the blue like that? It was so…so…what's the word?

What's the word? *Spontaneous.* Yes, that's it. It just popped into my head as natural as could be and instantly made complete sense. Then rolled out of my mouth like my tongue was made of silver. If that isn't a perfect definition of spontaneous, I don't know what is. And it turns out I was correct! I can't get over it. I can feel the shine in my own eyes. I bet that if I looked in a mirror, I'd see my eyes sparkling diamonds from feeling so good. If this is what confidence feels like, I'll take it. If this is what learning does for me, count me in.

112

Mary Patricia

Right here and right now, Mary Patricia is making an announcement: I promise myself to learn all that I can. I want to be — *I am* — a student, an actual student, a real learner. No ifs, ands, or buts about it. And it feels *grrrrrreat*. I'm learning stuff I never figured I could understand even if my life depended on it. Stuff I never even knew was there to find out about. Intuition, for instance. Which, if I do say so myself, I am finally getting the hang of. Figuring out that it's my intuition pushing and pulling inside me, egging me on, was a big step for me. And I'm working hard to understand what my intuition is trying to tell me.

Learning to recognize what's what is no walk in the park, that's for sure. Sometimes I get so irritated given the fact that things look about as clear as mud too often for my taste. And that's when I end up feeling as miserable as if I have wet sand in my underpants. And then I want to have a conniption and run away from it all like I used to do when I was in my old body. But I'm getting to learn the lay of the land around here, and I've seen that panic and throwing fits doesn't work — it only makes things worse. And by worse, I mean that it only puts off the inevitable. Because like it or not, sooner or later, facts have to be faced. That was a big, big lesson for me.

I was never good at facing facts when I was alive. That's one of my regrets. If I'd known you can't get out of it — no how, no way, not even if you're a poor, old, sick dead lady — maybe I would've done things differently. Maybe I could've found the courage somewhere, somehow to take charge of my life while I still had time. Believe you me, facing the music is as bound to happen as getting a bellyache after eating too many green apples. Dying doesn't change anything, I'll tell you that. Dead or alive, the more you don't want to face facts, the more your insides push you to. And the more your insides have to push you, the tougher it's going to be when you finally get around to it. I had to learn the hard way. If I could've faced facts sooner, dealt with things when they first started to go bad, I wouldn't have lost most of my life to misery I couldn't control. But how was I to know that anger and depression were big fat alarm bells when I was taught that time heals all wounds?

Keep your mouth shut and do nothing and whatever ails you will disappear on its own—that's what they always said. I didn't know the exact opposite is true: time really makes wounds a lot worse and leaves you with a sick heart. I see now that by avoiding the inevitable, I caused a lot of problems for myself and everybody else. Because one problem led to another like leaks in a dike, and soon I had a flood of troubles raining down on top of my shoulders and I felt like I was drowning in a slew of dirty clothes. And as exhausted as an old bag lady from the streets. And all I had left was rage.

Take it from me: forget about even *thinking* you can duck what you don't want to deal with. Do it now! Believe me, you'll save yourself a whole lot of time and aggravation, because the way it works is that everybody has to face facts anyway—including old dead ladies. You think it's easy being an old dead lady and dealing with all this stuff? I highly *do not* recommend it. Then again, who am I to say? I never listened to anybody's advice. But now I am listening to my own. And like it or lump it, I've been through enough struggles on this side to know that I have to keep pushing through those terrible awful feelings to get to what I need to understand. That's where the light comes in. Sunlight. Starlight. Daylight. Moonlight. Light bulb light. Feeling light. *Being* light. All that light—all that learning. All that understanding waiting at the end of a long, dark tunnel.

113

Mary Patricia

The woman in the fog offers me a cigarette. See? I knew I liked her. I inhale extra deep and blow out a soft cloud. I am so relaxed that I feel like a bowl of Jell-O. It seems strange to be this calm after all I've been through. But maybe not. I've been learning darn important things. Like how I'm not a crazy half-wit, and how according to what I surmise, I never have been. That warms my heart up something awful. I always figured that the naked truth about me was all bad—worse than bad. And facing facts meant I'd be torn apart limb by limb and left like vulture meat on the side of the road. Turns out I was wrong about that. I learned that facts I believed to be true facts when I was alive weren't true after all.

Remember Jack Webb in "Dragnet"? *Just the facts, ma'am, just the facts.* That's what they're into on this side—just the truth. The bottom line. The nitty-gritty. What's left when all is said and done. They don't have any use for the lies and rumors that raise Cain earthside, or for putting on hoity-toity airs. Also, here nobody caters to digs and insults. I found that out on my own. They don't go in for gossip, either. It's just not copacetic. There's a lot of respect for the individual. Hearts are drawn to love around here.

I didn't know that the real bottom-line facts about me are good—really good. Finding out that my brain really works and that I really am a good person even though a lot of times I didn't act that way? Boy was that a surprise to me. What a relief...*what a boost*...to know something like that about yourself. I sure wish I understood when I was living—really, really understood—that not everything about me was bad. In fact, that there was an awful lot of good about me—*an awful lot.* If only I could've known, then maybe things would've been different for me. And maybe if I could've understood that all that push and pull and nagging inside me was my *real self* speaking—my intuition—I could've learned to listen and worked up the courage to be a woman of action and done right by myself, instead of always cursing and criticizing every single thing I ever did. I know now that my intuition is the best compass, the best pair of glasses I could ever hope to own, and it lives to serve me, urging me to see and learn important things for my own benefit—and not to beat me up and force me to slave for everybody. Maybe if I had understood all this, I wouldn't have felt so lost and angry and been so ornery.

I take another long drag. This is one hell of a cigarette I'm enjoying, I'll tell you that. *Growth.* That word drifts out of the smoke cloud and settles over me like a mellow light. I never thought much about the word *growth* except for how tall my kids were getting. But I hear it a lot around here. Except they use the word *growthment.* I never paid much attention, because *growthment* didn't make any sense to me. But I'm starting to get the drift. More than get the drift. It's starting to sink in that *growthment* means progress, personal progress. And little by little, I'm making progress—I am growing.

It's a funny thing for an old dead lady to say, but *I am growing up...* finally. It's taken long enough, but it's finally happening: I am growing up. And I'm doing it through learning. I'm starting to see things with my heart instead of with my anger. I'm learning to see *myself* with my heart. I'm learning to see with light instead of dragging everything through the gutter. I'm learning that my intuition is a form of...a form of...let me say love. Love in the way of treating somebody good...with kindness... with a warm heart. Intuition is me loving me. Doesn't that sound weird coming from me, a woman who hated herself? But it's the honest truth: *my intuition is me loving me.* I see that now. My intuition is me working for me. It's not the devil torturing me, wanting to push my face in the mud. Or God slapping me around, giving me what for. I'm getting used to how this operates now. How when my intuition is driving me to deal with something I don't want to deal with, it's not punishing me. It's the *me* inside of *me* loving *me*...wanting, needing to see; to grow; to learn; to understand...to progress so I get to feel better and better. To feel and be healthy, I guess I'd say. And to generate more and more light for myself. Not that I know what I'm going to do with all this light...

I have regrets, a lot of them. I wish things had been better. I wish with all my heart that I'd done a lot of things differently—I've done a lot of stuff that I'm not proud of and I'm really, really sorry for that. I wish I'd been a happy person when I was alive. I wanted to be, but I just couldn't make it work. What I've learned on this side though is that nothing good can come out of me tormenting myself over past mistakes. That self-torment is fatal. They are teaching me that thoughts are *real* things, *powerful* things that can make or break you according to how much you concentrate on them. Not too long ago, I saw a poor soul with so many negative thoughts glued to her back that she's bent over like a cripple. They're working with her, but she's got a long way to go.

I'm finished concentrating on all the negative things about myself. What I can do now is learn from the past and march forward. And believe you me, *I am*. Words can't do justice for how really, really excited I am about growing and learning...and having intuition. You can't imagine how much I like all of this. Excuse me...*how much I love all of this*. I can hardly believe that intuition actually belongs to *me*. That I actually have it. That Mary Patricia has her very own intuition. That Mary Patricia has always had her very own intuition. *And it's real*. Not in a trillion years would I have known this. Or believed it. And I'll tell you something else: I promise to listen to it. And follow it, too. Really listen. Really follow. No holds barred.

Right here and right now, I'm making another announcement: I am going to trust my intuition. I am going to trust myself. I am going to do it. I want to do it. I want to learn to really use it. I'm hell-bent for election about this. Nobody can stop me when I put my mind to something. That is one thing I know unequivocally about myself.

Though I have to confess, I'm sensing something, because I'm beginning to feel a little upset. There's something underneath my excitement. Something ruffling it. Something not too nice. Something full and willful. Like a blind pimple poking up from under your skin. How it's tender and sore. And you know without looking that something's not quite right.

I don't like it.

114

Mary Patricia

I sure wish that blind pimple sensation weren't there, because I like feeling excited and fired up. And I don't want to take a chance on messing things up. Because what if my good feelings about my intuition and trusting myself are murdered by bad thoughts? And what if those bad thoughts kill all my good chances at becoming who I want to be? Who I know I can be now without Ornery Pat calling all the shots? *Who I really am?*

There goes my good mood, taking a nosedive into the dirt. My heart is caving in. It's heavier and heavier, too heavy to carry. My chest...it's hard to breathe. I knew it...Ornery Pat is here, waiting in the wings to take over. Why is this happening? I don't understand. I feel her anger ratcheting up just like before. She's squeezing me. Tightening the noose. It's clogging my throat, her anger is. She's itching for a fight. *I know it. I feel it.* The only thing she needs is a trigger—something to carry on about, something to destroy. All I have to do is give her an inch and she's off to the races. And I'm back where I started, with Ornery Pat leading the way.

I clap my hands over my ears. I can't believe I'm shouting, "Get out of here! Get out of here!", like some crazy woman on a bender trying to fend off little green men. It takes me a second to remember that *I am not crazy.* That what I am is aggravated—and you better believe I'm aggravated at how Ornery Pat keeps taking a buzz saw to my nerves. I've had enough of her shenanigans. But crazy? No siree, Bob. Not a chance. Not on your life. But by hook or by crook, I have to find a way to get rid of her. How, though, how? Lay into her with cusswords that would curl a sailor's hair and scare her off? Chase her away with screams loud enough to knock the woman in the fog off her chair and turn that glow into mud? Slap her so silly she wouldn't be able to see straight, and run her off with my fists? Do you know how easy that no-sweat, old hat, kid stuff would be for me? In my old life, I gave more people the boot than I can name.

But this isn't my old life anymore and I'm coming to see things more clearly. I want to remember that. That's the hardest part, since I'm still not totally accustomed to the fact that the tactics I used to use don't work here. I have to keep reminding myself that nowadays, I am an actual cogitating person. A sincere, committed learner. So, I take a minute, breathe the good breath, and let the dust settle. And my heart flutters with a solution. It's so basic. So simple. *Just keep cleaning up my act*—my mental act. Wash and vacuum away all my destructive habits. Clear out all the ways of destroying myself. Freshen everything up just like I used to do to this house I'm sitting in, only now I'm refreshing myself. So there it is—an answer from my own heart. From my personal intuition. How about that? There all the time, I surmise. I have to admit that I'm amazed at how this intuition stuff works. Dazed but not confused. I want more.

115

Mary Patricia

I stare at the smoke coiling from my Raleigh, thin strands that remind me of thread. "And what does thread do?" I ask myself, not really expecting an answer. But the answer appears in the blink of an eye: *thread stitches pieces of cloth together.* No sooner do I conclude that then I sense a softening and loosening of something rock hard and enormous in my lower regions. Something I had no clue was stuck there until this very moment. The way it feels, I'd call it a huge chunk of concrete crumbling and dissolving, melting into a soothing flow. Not a rush like a plug's been pulled. And not a trickling. But a smooth, calm flow of...of...liquid light. That's the best I can say. The flow has a warm presence like a moving, breathing glow. It's alive. It's a real living thing. It's...oh, what's the word I'm looking for? Illum...illuminate... *illuminated.* That's it! *Illumination.* Yes, that's what I'm trying to get at...*living illumination*—a moving, breathing glow. Hold your horses, because I'm having a brainstorm. I can't believe I'm deducing this, but I am. *Living illumination*: the glow of intuition flowing along in a stream of rising knowledge.

Never! Never in all my days could I imagine me coming up with something like that. Good grief, can this really be *me*? Am I actually talking like this? Thinking like this? Figuring this stuff out on my own? A woman who never even finished high school? I'm shaking. Excuse me, I have to have another cigarette.

I always felt like I was the dumbest of the dumb. Worthless. I need time to get used to this. To get used to me, Mary Patricia, construing something so lofty. When I was alive, my daydreams could never even dream a dream this fantastic as me cogitating and actually deducing something I presumed only an egghead could understand. I never counted on myself to deduce anything, much less anything highbrow. Can this really be true?

I sit back, pull more smoke from my Raleigh, and let all my figuring settle. This is really beyond words what I'm messing around with here. Who am I—a high school dropout from the squat town of Fieldsboro with its town drunk and rundown houses—to be thinking in ways always left to people better than me? I *do* feel like that scarecrow from *The Wizard of Oz* with arithmetic equations pouring out of his brain. I'm wrestling with matters of life and death…and figuring them out! Do you hear me? I'm figuring them out! And I'm scared…because things are starting to make so much sense to me, and I don't understand how *I* can possibly own the kind of intelligence that grasps…I have to say *concepts*, a word I never used in my life. Big concepts, big thoughts. Why I—me, of all people, dumbest of the dumb—am starting to key into the kind of learning I could never even begin to fathom when I was earthside.

Like how death means a lot more than just the body checking out. How death also has to do with a mind and a spirit giving up long before the body hands in the towel. Which I know I did when I was on the other side. And all this news is agreeing with me. The more it rings true, the more my heart cheers, *YES, Mary Patricia! WAY TO GO!* I feel like I'm not lurking on the sidelines anymore. I'm running the race. And the more I run, the faster and farther I want to go.

But I still can't help feeling like a deer in the headlights. *I'm frightened, Auntie Em, I'm frightened.* Not of some cardboard bogeyman, or the devil in my head, but scared to death of myself. Of my brain. Like it's exploded with dictionary smarts and high-minded understanding. And this isn't really me. *It can't be me.* How can it be me? How can it? Where is all this coming from? What if I'm a fake? What if everything is fake? What if I'm really as dead as a doornail, no more than ashes buried six feet under, and I'm bobbing around in a weird suspended animation situation until my ashes settle down and bite the dirt?

I screw my face into a dark, bitter scowl and look over at the woman in the fog. If she can't see how unhappy I am and how much I need her to open her mouth and tell me what to do, then she's deader than I am. I could've guessed…she's cool, calm, and collected. Cool as a cucumber, I'd say for lack of a better description. And she's not taking my bait. In fact, she's unfazed by my sulking antics. I'd call her downright peaceful, as if all is well. As if I'm well. *As if I'm well.* Those words pulse faintly against my heart...gong...gong...gong... Chills flood through me, into every nook and cranny of this body of mine. Up and down my spine. Raising the hair on my arms, on the back of my neck. Filling me with fizz and pep. And blazing starlight. I am like a thirsty sponge soaking up sparkling water. Only the water is a whisper of glowing words: *As if I'm well.*

I've never been what you would call *well*. I never expected to be. It's not like I didn't want to be well; it's just that nothing ever worked out good for me. But now...now... Maybe I am well. Maybe I am fine. I inhale another good breath without the smoke. Then another. And it strikes me: *I am fine.* And I am going to be fine. The whisper deep inside tells me this. Assures me... Then I do something unheard of...*I decide that it's true.* I decide that I am fine. I take the wheel—and turn my frown upside down, just like I used to tell my kids—and decide that I am fine. I am A-okay. I hear myself say, *You're fine*: YOU. ARE. FINE. And I feel it—I feel "fine" tap dancing in my bones. I feel the weightless wings of "fine" in the gentle breeze surrounding me. *I am fine. I am going to be fine.* I want to sing these words from the rooftop. I want to tap dance to their music.

The woman in the fog smiles at me. Her smile looks as bright as mine feels. *Maybe she's an angel.* Maybe I'm an angel. Nobody in my old life would've ever called me an angel, that's for sure. But I'm starting to feel like one. Not an angel with fluffy wings playing a trumpet. Weightless like an angel. Feather-light. And filled with light. Illuminated. That's it, lightened with illumination. The illumination of...of...knowledge. It's changing me, knowledge is. No, not changing me...*transforming* me. From an ugly duckling into a beautiful swan. What do you think of that?

I close my eyes and breathe long slow breaths and exhale all the way down to my toes. I listen to my heart speak. It comforts me. It reassures me that what I am learning is very important. *Vitally important, in fact.* What I am learning is life giving. None of it is lofty or over my head. My heart is inviting me to be with my new-found self. To sit still and listen to my own voice. This voice...*my voice*...whispers that I alone know what is best for me—*I alone.*

Such rest comes over me. Such peace, I can't even explain. I feel as if I'm hearing my favorite music again. A song I haven't heard in a dog's age. One I loved so much but that's been lost to me. Then I forgot all about it. But now hearing that song once again, I remember every single word. And I still get goose bumps. My heart still skips a beat. The music has come back to me. I recognize it. I recognize my voice. My heart's voice... I stare at the smoke still coiling from my cigarette. Thin strands of thread.

116

Mary Patricia

They drowned me in the river.

It's a story I never told. My heart's beating so fast just thinking about it, about how they threw me in the Delaware. I feel like the story is right here in my forehead, trying to burst out into the open. Trying to get heard. It's a thought string…a thread…anxious to be pulled…

I remember it all. I remember my nose. How it stung. The water rushing up and burning my nostrils. The searing pain. The icy water boring into my brain. I was burning alive. I was freezing to death.

I want to listen to it. I want to hear my story. I want to see what happened to me. I want to understand.

I want a storyteller.

117

Kathleen

I've been a storyteller for as long as I can remember—a storyteller forbidden to tell stories. In a family culture of silence and secrets, stories are cursed, the truth permanently banned. And so it is that intentional cruelties and cruel misjudgments capable of inflicting lifelong destruction end up ignored, the victim of those brutalities disregarded, her injuries not only unimportant but never even acknowledged. It requires a lot of courage to acknowledge the catastrophic consequences forced on a person— a child—by heartless behavior or careless deeds. Mary Patricia's people were not courageous. And Mary Patricia suffered for it.

Surely her parents didn't mean for their young daughter to drown in the Delaware that sweltering midsummer afternoon. Why should they? All their other children swam for their lives the moment their bodies hit the river. Sink or swim, that was the modus operandi of the time—the *either-you're-going-to-get-those-arms-and-legs-moving-or-you're-going-to-drown* technique for teaching kids to swim. Probably the part about sinking was bluster, though maybe not. What if when a kid was too stupid to swim, parents just yawned and mused: *Guess we found the dumb one; sank faster than a rock. They just don't make kids like they used to.* With that kind of attitude, it would be no surprise if the bottom of the Delaware is to this day littered with the bones of uncoordinated dimwits from the '30s and '40s—kids who never could figure out how to turn their arms and legs into fins. Or brats who, just for spite, defied their parents and drowned on purpose. Which if you knew Patsy's temperament, could have been her. Only it wasn't. Patsy was petrified of that river.

Not for one instant did the Delaware River lure Patsy. Not like it did her brothers, who were rowdy and fearless and imagined themselves Davy Crockett, carrying sticks that looked like muskets if you squinted hard enough and sounded like them, too, if you shouted *bang* loud enough.

Carried still on the distant winds are the phantom echoes of the Evans boys staging endless cowboy and Indian raids in the brush near the river. What better place for youngsters to go on the warpath than a riverbank? Eyes peeled, clapped onto the Pennsylvania shoreline, jumping up and down, shouting, "Swear to God! Swear to God! There's a brave in those bulrushes over there! An Apache! In war paint and buckskin! With a bow and arrow! Aimed at us!"

Unlike her brothers, Patsy never clenched a plastic Bowie knife between her teeth or inched into the murky water intent on capturing Indians on the other side. She did not don torn dungarees and striped polo shirts and slither through mud and slime smelling of little kid sweat and decaying fish to scout out the enemy across the river. It raked across her nerves, that river did, and fired up her instincts warning her of its depth, of the currents that ran hard and frigid as it patiently waited to drag a child under, only so it could shoot the small body through its murky undercurrents, sailing it like a wobbly bullet clear down to the bay hundreds of miles south before anyone could attempt a rescue.

No, Patsy was no tomboy. She had other proclivities—girly proclivities—that kept her entertained. While her brothers crawled through tall grasses on their bellies, Patsy, a big satin bow tied atop her Shirley Temple curls, spun daydreams alone in her room, contenting herself with cutting out paper dolls from romance magazines and quietly pacing them through dramas she'd invented. If she had a mind to, she could stretch her thin body across her bed on a hot afternoon and stare up at the ceiling Mother had painted midnight blue and decorated with stars hand-cut from tinfoil. When the sun tilted just right and beamed bright through the window, those stars twinkled against that make-believe night sky just like in a planetarium. It was a good place for the imaginations of a little girl.

The river was no place for a child with Patsy's sensitivities. The walk down the hill to the Delaware was eerie and deserted except for old Mrs. Douglas's house at the bottom that emerged from the haze and tangled brambles looking like a crematory waiting to snatch bodies. The jagged stones that littered the shore stabbed tender feet, and cold mud oozed up between small toes and dried scaly and crusty on soft skin. Not to mention the chilled, lapping water that raced goose bumps up bare legs despite scorching heat. That river bristled Patsy's nerves and awakened sinister fears that foretold dangers she couldn't explain. So, they may as well have been trying to pull teeth with slippery fingers that day *they* tried to coax her down to its edge.

They tried plying her with candy. Patsy didn't like candy. They made promises. They'd take her to the movies, to Atlantic City. Patsy favored staying in her bedroom playing with her dolls. They pleaded. If she'd just take a walk with them, they'd have a picnic afterwards. Fried chicken and potato salad. And Mother's special sweet iced tea. And for dessert, Daddy's potato donuts that he brought home from the bakery where he worked. Patsy didn't really care much about food. What finally won her over was the magic of sweet talk and flattery.

Did she know there was a pirate's chest full of gold and precious gems buried down the river just waiting to be found? *She* could help them find the treasure. After all, who was smarter than Patsy? Nobody, that's who. She was as sharp as a whip. As clever as a fox. A regular Dick Tracy, by God. All she had to do was help them find the gold and they'd all be rich. Patsy could have all the dolls her heart desired, and Mother could have diamonds and furs! Imagine that! And Patsy did imagine that... Patsy imagined the big smile lighting up Mother's face when they gave her all the gold and precious gems in the world.

The rowboat, sitting half in, half out of the water, was no more than bleached driftwood patched together with rusty nails. *The treasure's out there,* they said, using sticks to point to the current rippling down the middle of the river. *That's where the ship sank. That's where the treasure chest is.* But something wasn't right. Patsy heard it in their voices. They sounded wrong. Different. Too loud. Too screechy. Too high pitched. Voices straight out of a circus sideshow. Voices hawking tickets for the two-headed baby and the fattest woman in the world. Voices that plunged Patsy's stomach into free fall and got her legs quivering with nameless fear.

She balked, pulling against an invisible leash, her body stiff and fixed, refusing to move. They tried soft-soaping her into the boat. *What about the gold we're going to find? Don't you want to make Mother happy?* When she tried inching away, one of them grabbed her hands, restraining her from running back home, back to safety. Hefty arms, strong enough to bear the eruption of thrashing fists and rigid, kicking feet, wrangled Patsy's dead weight into the slapdash boat. *There's nothing to be afraid of. We're going to find pirate gold.* Her shrieking, fevered panic surged and swelled, attacking the silence. Her screams clawing and bellowing in a free-for-all stampede across the wet grave of the Delaware River ricocheted back to shore and up Delaware Avenue and into her tiny bedroom with the tinfoil stars glittering against the night sky ceiling.

Come on, Patsy, come on, now, they said, and plunked her down on a plank inside the rowboat, restricting her with muscles and promises sugared with visions of vast riches. The sour taste of terror filmed her tongue and dried the roof of her mouth. She gulped the thick, curdled pulp clogging her throat. Gurgling. Swallowing. Gurgling. Swallowing. The only breath she could muster wheezed out as a weak cry atop a thread of sticky air. She wanted to keep screaming her bloody head off. But her screams had vanished, abandoning her to the mercy of her restrainers and the rough wood and cold water. Leaving eight-year-old Patsy powerless amid the commotion of blathering and the madness of terror locked inside her, lodged between her hipbones, burning acid craters inside her belly.

Her small, ashen hands clung to the rutted wood, her delicate knuckles blanched white as she tried to steel herself against the hitch and lurch of the boat rocking side to side across the currents, the oars squeaking and scraping, splashing quietly into the water that sloshed and slurped against the hull as if licking its chops waiting for her. The motion repeatedly slid her stomach down toward her knees, then heaved it upward again and again until bile was blowtorching a hole into the back of her throat—her petite features shrunken, drained of color, tinged chlorotic green. She was a crazed animal, at once shivering and sweating, trapped in a snare beneath the scorching rays of the sun.

Look, Patsy. Look down there. There's the treasure. Swim for it, Patsy.

Swim for it... The last words she heard before hands hoisted her and hurled her skyward, high, high enough that she stared wildly into the eyes of the sun.

Airborne, her body was an arced and fleeting silhouette against the lit heavens, pitching and tossing like a torn kite. She plunged down, down. Spits of ice water stung her legs just before total impact. Then belly first, she slammed into the river that besieged her with its wet, deep freeze, ripping the breath from her lungs, swapping it for blue hot fire, strangled screams, and thrashing bones.

What burst through the surface of the Delaware River on that day that Patsy drowned was no longer human .

118

Mary Patricia

Oh…no. Oh no. Oh no. It hurts. It hurts. *It hurts…*

119

Mary Patricia

How long I've been sitting here, I don't know...*I don't know.* Just waterworks and dry heaves. And fire from the river water burning the inside of my nose just like it did then. You can't imagine this pain. *You can't...* It's worse than pain. It's agony screaming from every pore. For days and days, this agony's been gushing out of me like poison, like green pus. *I see it. I see it.* I'm looking into its bloodthirsty eyes. I smell its stench. Putrid like garbage baking under the blazing sun. It's a being...a monster, an actual, living monstrosity. Smoke dripping venom, but with a shape. It looks like an ogre rising from the mist in an old-time horror film. Twisted and bent. Hunchbacked. Gnarled. Deformed by carbuncles and the hideous knobs of rheumatoid arthritis. Skin chewed raw by flesh-eating boils.

This is what was living inside me all that time? This is what was eating me alive? This is what depression looks like on the inside? This is the sight of anguish? This is fear turned mad?

Did it kill me? Am I alive? Or am I dead? I don't know. I don't know. *Breathe, Mary Patricia, breathe.*

120

Mary Patricia

I'm shocked numb. Stunned as if somebody whacked the side of my head with a frying pan and knocked me out. Finally I'm coming out of my stupor. Starting to breathe regular again without having to concentrate. I'm waking up. But not from sleep or being knocked senseless. I'm waking up to why I could never face the real truth about the horrible things that people did to me: throwing me in the river, raping me. It would've been torture to think about the actual details, the true hard facts. Too much god-awful pain.

I'm recognizing now that those horrible incidents turned into some kind of terrifying, monstrous black force in my mind that held a gun to my head and forbid me to tell. It patrolled my thoughts, that black force did—I didn't even allow myself to have bad feelings over all that awful stuff. That black force dragged me away and locked me up for good.

For your own good—that's what the black force in my mind yelled at me. *If you dare open your big mouth, you'll be put to shame. Called a liar. And everybody upon everybody will condemn you. If anybody ever finds out that you are accusing decent people of hurting you, if you dare let any tears show, everybody will turn their backs on you and you'll be sent packing so fast it'll make your head spin. And you'll have nobody. You'll end up in rags begging on the streets of Trenton getting beaten up every day of the week.*

That's what the black force said. That's what my mind said.

Breathe, Mary Patricia, breathe.

121

Mary Patricia

I didn't just die yesterday, you know. I've been around the block a few times in this place. And I've come to know that nothing is given, all is earned. I guess I'm earning my wings by how I'm understanding things better than I ever did. There's a font inside me now—a reservoir, I guess you'd call it. A reservoir of experiences that I'm dipping into and looking at and tying together so that things make sense to me. I'm starting to feel something inside me. Something like a pillar. Something strong that is holding me in place. But more than that, it's making me tall. Not in the way of height, because I've always been a small woman. But tall like a person with a backbone. Tall in the saddle, I think I mean. I'm strong and getting stronger because of this pillar. The pillar is…well, it's all my experiences fusing together with my understanding of them.

I never knew anything about this kind of stuff. How learning about your experiences—learning about them all the way down to your toes—gives you something. Not give in the way of a handout, like how I always expected prayers to give me whatever it was I was praying for. No, not like that at all. Give in the way of…of ability. That's a better description. Learning about your experiences gives you…oh my good grief… learning about your experiences gives you *power*. Can you believe it? Can you believe it? Power, of all words. I'm earning my power…*I'm earning my power.* Oh good grief. Me. Mary Patricia. Powerful. Oh good grief, for all the money in all the world, I could never, ever have imagined this… *me* being—*actually being*—powerful. I want to repeat it a zillion times, because I'm stunned at the truth of this development. That it's really, really true. That I'm not just saying words. Or playing stupid. Or playing wishy-washy games with myself and other people by talking big but not meaning a word of it. Or expecting somebody else, including God, to do for me what I wouldn't do for myself.

It's come true, after all this time—it's come true. And I did it myself! There's power inside me now...a pillar of power...one I created...one I earned. It's like looking at myself in the mirror after lifting weights for a long time and being shocked by my muscles. *Can you believe it? Can you believe it?* It's come true. And I did it myself!

122

Mary Patricia

Soon I'll be leaving this house...my house...here on Mark Twain Drive. I'm not going to miss it. Don't get me wrong, I'll always love this place. It's full of so many good times and memories. But I'm itching to go. There are things I want to do. More I want to learn. I can't do it here.

I settle back and pick up my pack of Raleighs. I love the sound of crinkling cellophane. To a smoker, it's the call of beautiful music. A coupon is still glued to the back. I collected hundreds over the years and turned them over for lots of neat stuff for my house...towels, pots and pans, knickknacks. I pull out a cigarette. One last one. The woman in the fog leans over and lights it for me. It still tastes so damn good. So damn good. She pours fresh coffee into my mug. It's too hot to drink, but I take a sip anyhow. It burns so good on the way down. Staring into the twilight, I feel as relaxed as a baggy sweater.

"I am my own encyclopedia," I say to the woman in the fog. She nods, reaches out, and touches my hand. Hers is as warm as toast. "You know, by studying all I've been through, I've learned that I survived my life by racing around in one tight, endless circle: I ate the pain. The pain ate me."

Out of the corner of my eye, I catch the look on the woman in the fog's face. It's life-and-death serious. She's listening to me in a way that I'm unaccustomed to. Nobody really ever took me seriously when I was alive. She leans forward and locks her gaze on my eyes and it hits me that not once in all my time here have her eyes ever run away from me.

I take a puff of my cigarette. I need to cogitate on this state of affairs. I have to think about this—really think. I have to really take it to heart that the woman in the fog accepts me, warts and all. I have to allow myself to believe that she is here for me for better or worse. She's proved it. She's put up with my ranting and raving without ever flinching. That says something.

That really, really says something. Most people couldn't wait to get away from me.

"The pain I had to stomach," I say to her, trying not to let my voice crack, "no matter how much I hurt, was no great shakes to anybody around me. It didn't matter how much somebody hurt me or the rotten things they did to me that drove me to ruin. It didn't count how terrible I was breaking apart or suffering. All that mattered was keeping my mouth shut. And keeping my mouth shut—especially keeping my mouth shut to myself—killed me. It just up and killed me. No ifs, ands, or buts about it."

The air around me is still, yet electrified. I *feel* the tears sliding down my friend's cheeks as if they were rolling down my own. I *hear* her heart beating in time with mine. She wants to hear my story. *I feel it.* I *feel* her compassion, her understanding, and my heart overflows with love for her—my dear, dear friend, the woman in the fog. I take both her hands in mine. I am not accustomed to expressing love, but her love is radiating into my soul, melting into me like warm sunshine. I *want* to return love to her.

"I don't know how to thank you in words," I whisper. "I've always been so terrified to bare my soul. People have turned on me, and I'm so afraid that you will, too. But I want to take a chance." My heart's beating double time. *Just say it, Mary Patricia, I tell myself. YOU. ARE. FINE. You're doing grrrreattt!*

I look straight into my dear friend's eyes. And take a deep, deep breath. "You mean more to me than I can even say. You saved my life. Do you know that?" She looks down at our hands, then up into my eyes again. I have to keep talking or I'll break down from her kindness. "You listened to every word I've said. I felt like you were hearing me with your heart. You stood by my side when I've had my conniptions, and you never ran away. Not once. You held my hand and encouraged me to look at what I did not want to see. And what I didn't think I could face.

"You had faith in me. That means more to me than I can ever tell. You held me up when I couldn't hold myself up. Never once did you get aggravated. I want you to know that when my nerves got the best of me, your calmness helped me calm down. You never cringed or rolled your

eyes when I talked and talked and talked. Or got your bowels in an uproar when I raged at the air in front of me and fought every step I took."

She smiles and squeezes my hands. She must be some kind of angel. "You never made fun of me," I continue. "Or condemned me. Or shamed me. Your patience, your kindness, helped me to start being patient and kind with myself. And that's how I began learning to understand things. That's how I came to see that my words were stolen from me—actually stolen. No different from if a robber bound and gagged me and stole all my jewelry. I had a terrible time accepting that. That such a thing could happen to a person. And that the person could not even know it. It's hard figuring out something you can't see with your eyes. And learning about abuse. Learning that *abuse* is a word that applies to me. *To me.* It still feels funny saying that I was subjected to abuse, because I always just figured that's the way things were and you had to forget about all the bad stuff. But forgetting never was going to work—never, ever, ever. I could say that a hundred times a hundred, because that's how true it is. You don't forget about abuse, and abuse sure doesn't forget about you. Abuse destroyed me. It destroyed Mary Patricia before she even had a chance."

We are silent for a while. And I am smiling for all the things I understand now. I feel like a puppy in love. I feel *right*, like I have a place in this world. Like I have a place in my own life. Like I fit in my own shoes, finally. And I feel brave! Like I've marched off to war and come back a hero, scars and all—I've defeated the enemy! If I was a drinking woman, I'd have a few to celebrate my victory. I don't hit the booze anymore. But I'm drinking in the kick of having my words back. I'm drunk with the thrill of understanding things I didn't know anything about. Understanding things is giving me a bigger buzz than any I ever got from hooch. Though I admit that if you twisted my arm, I wouldn't refuse a screwdriver.

"I see now that the real me, Mary Patricia, was abandoned—shut off and shut down," I say, breaking the silence. "Good grief, I was so scared for so much of my life. I was the mouse running away from the cat, even when the cat wasn't chasing me. What I understand now is that when I couldn't run far enough away inside myself, Ornery Pat came blasting out of the gun full of piss and vinegar, rearing to come to the rescue. She was a handful—that I can't deny. But I *liked* that she was a firecracker full of spunk. Ornery Pat made me feel strong, like I could take on the world. Only what I didn't exactly notice was what a disaster she was.

They say that hindsight is 20/20. I realize now that the charge I got out of Ornery Pat getting all revved up and coming out guns blazing looking for a fight only lasted a little while. Because once Ornery Pat got going, she'd get out of control and do things I was ashamed of. After she was on a roll, there was no way I could stop her. There was nothing anybody could do to stop her. She was all antics. And I felt so ashamed afterward. Ashamed because I figured people would respect me for not taking any guff. But everybody just looked at me like I was an embarrassment to them, a burden they didn't know what to do with. I never knew how to make things right after Ornery Pat made a mess. I usually ended up only making things worse, and that made me feel even more ashamed."

I pull two Raleighs out of the pack. One more last one for me and one for my friend. There's nothing like a good cigarette, I'll tell you that. Satisfyingly delicious—that's the best way to describe it. Partners for a lot of years, me and cigarettes were. Wherever I was, there were my cigarettes. They never left one speck of cancer in my lungs, either. I'll be leaving them behind, too. But right now, I'm thinking about my last first drag, and that tickles my funny bone. I feel as giddy as a little girl. *Light me up, friend,* I say to the woman in the fog. She does and we both take long, deep drags. Forget about anything else, *this is heaven.* I spot my friend purse her lips into a big O and watch her blow out enormous smoke rings. I laugh until my ribs ache. Over the years, I too was a champion smoke-ring blower, so I puff out a few fat samples of my own. Sun is all around us. The light floods me inside and out.

I have the odd sensation of my throat opening up. I actually feel the muscles shift and the hum of my voice vibrating. I close my eyes and witness the music of my voice unfold like a blossom and flower into bright light. This isn't an imaginary thing. It is something that is really happening to me. I am blooming. It strikes me: my voice is part of the harmony of light around me…within me. *I feel it.* I know it. As I for certain live and breathe in this place I knew nothing about when I was alive, I now know for sure that my voice is music. My voice is poetry. *My voice is nature.* As right as the songs of birds. As right as the sound of the wind. My voice—Mary Patricia's voice—is part of everything living. Here. There. An important part. As important as air. As important as light.

The overwhelming urge to speak floods my chest and wells up into my throat. Automatically I clamp my mouth shut and start forcing the words back down my gullet like I used to do. But I pause and remember the light, the poetry, the music. *Breathe, Mary Patricia, breathe.*

"Here's what I think," I say with confidence, positive now that my voice is my music and that I have to use it if I want to be heard. "Fear is a disease. A terrible, terrible infection. It spreads through your whole body like arsenic until it kills off all the good stuff. Good thoughts. Good feelings. Good health."

My friend looks at me and nods like I'm onto something…something important. I wish I didn't have a nagging inside me warning me to keep quiet—warning me that Mary Patricia doesn't have the intelligence to know anything about this subject, or any other for that matter. I breathe in and breathe out. Slow and steady. Again and again. I no longer have to wrestle for control, but I still have to intentionally keep myself together and remind myself about what I know. And I know now that I'm bigger than the remnants of my fear and that I have to push it away if I'm going to keep growing. Or go through it. Or around it. Or under it. Somehow or other, I have to wave bye-bye to my old bad nerves and keep going—no exceptions.

It's hard to do, but I have things to say. Things I've cogitated on long and hard. And I want to say them out loud. *I'm going to say them out loud.* I can't let fear stop me. If I do, I'll be back racing around in that tight, endless circle of pain. I've already done that. I know that leads exactly nowhere. And I'm ready to move on.

123

Mary Patricia

"Time's a-wastin'," I say to the woman in the fog. "I need to put on my dancing shoes and get going. I have things to do and places to go." My friend nods. We understand each other. I walk over to the stove and pick up the coffeepot. It's empty, in need of a good scrubbing. I grab a Brillo pad from under the sink. Some water hot enough to scald my hands because that's the way I've always liked it, a few squirts of Joy, a little elbow grease, and it's starting to look brand new. Back when I was alive, I loved to wash dishes. It saved my sanity. Gave me time to contemplate.

My friend is tinkering around, emptying the ashtray in the garbage, wiping the scattered ashes off the table. She moseys over, puts our mugs in the sink, and grabs a dishtowel. I hand her the coffeepot to dry and start gathering things off the shelves and out of the cabinets and drawers. Dusty knickknacks. My collection of salt and pepper shakers. Silverware. Candy dishes. Nothing expensive. All goodies from my Raleigh coupon days. Just touching them again warms the cockles of my heart. You forget so much. Washing dishes—this is my kind of heaven. I wash. The woman in the fog dries.

"I had to decipher what fear was. Does that make sense?" I ask my friend. The look in her eyes tells me yes. "I have to remember to appreciate that I never recognized myself as a fearful person. I never noticed what fear was doing to me day in and day out. I never recognized those terrible awful feelings of bad nerves as anything to do with fear. And that getting so damn mad and frustrated and having one of my conniption fits and acting really really mean was anything other than me just having a tantrum because I was a horrible woman. Never in all my life did I know about such a thing as trauma and what it does to a person."

Suddenly, tears as hot as the scalding dishwater are rushing down my cheeks. "If I had known, I could have saved my children," I whisper. I'm near to collapsing from the agony of what I now *see*. Buried memories come flashing back. My sons' little-boy screams. The sad, lost eyes of my daughter. A storm of guilt and sorrow lurch and churn inside my gut. My legs are watery. I feel seasick. I am reliving frightening scenes and my throat is gagged, blocked, frozen, as worthless now as it was then. I am witnessing incidents again that shouldn't have happened to my children but did. Incidents I should never have kept silent about. I should have fought mountains for my kids, stood up for them more. But I didn't. *I couldn't.* I couldn't budge. And I don't know *why*.

I am remembering the physical beatings of my sons that I refused to recognize as abuse, the constant verbal insults hurled at all of them that I just chalked off as jokes. Remembering the hidden cruelty I sensed was happening to my daughter that I closed my eyes to. I should have listened to my gut and stepped in to help—I could have protected her. Instead, I held my tongue, took the easy way out, and blamed her. I ignored too many situations with my children that made me sick to my stomach, swept them right under the rug so I didn't have to look at them. And pretended everything was fine when it wasn't.

I need to be condemned to hell for all my failures. I wish with every part of me that I was really dead. Deader than dead. I wish dead meant actually being dead and buried under mounds of dirt where you see and feel nothing. I can't bear this pain of my living past, of being the know-nothing see-nothing bystander mother while my children suffered something terrible.

How did that happen? I want to knock myself in the head with a damn hammer. How did it happen? What the hell was wrong with me that I stood silently by while my sons were being beaten and tormented, my daughter abused and raped? I stagger over to the table and slump into a chair. How could I have let that happen?

124

Mary Patricia

The woman in the fog is standing behind me. I am quaking so much that my brain is rattling inside my skull. I am nothing but an old, wasted bag of bones clanking together in hopeless grief over what I can never change. What I'll never have a chance to make up for. Anyhow, how can you make up for what's already been done? Or not done? I want to curl up in a ball and disappear as if I never existed.

My friend's soft tender hands rest on my shoulders, warming me like a blanket. They seem like the hands of an angel. I don't fight. In fact, I melt against her, so worn out from my troubles, and inhale the love and kindness coming from her like life-giving oxygen. All thoughts inside me stop. It's as if I am getting a transfusion—that's the best way to explain it. Her tenderness transports me beyond my heartbroken self. Her kind-heartedness is settling my nerves, loosening my muscles. It is seeping into my blood. Slowly, my heart begins to soften. My frozen throat is thawing. I sense a breath of light inching upward, shining the tiniest sunray that I squint into as hard as I can, willing it to grow bigger and bigger, to shine brighter and brighter.

My words tumble out sounding strange and hollow, distant echoes from this alien sun. "I was numbed to suffering. My own and everybody else's." I am croaking like a frog, uttering words I have never heard before. Words I have never thought, or said. Yet they are here, calling out to me like ghosts released from their graves. *I was numbed to suffering. My own and everybody else's.*

"That's it, isn't it?" My voice is hoarse, burnt, burned to a crisp. "That's it, isn't it?" I repeat. I repeat it because these words are punching me in the solar plexus—two fists to the gut. *Numbed to suffering.* They are a gong sounding in my head—a deep tolling of truth.

I have to think. I have to think. Breathe, Mary Patricia, breathe.

Too much is swirling around in my brain. Too much to organize. I'm overwhelmed. I *have* to talk it out. I *have* to understand this. My friend stands quietly behind me, her hands still warm and comforting. I am more thankful for her than I can ever express. *Deep breath. Deep breath.* Her hand squeezes my shoulder. "In my mind," I finally manage, "pain and suffering were always faked, used to get sympathy. To get over on somebody. Pain meant nothing to me. Body pain, heart pain—it was all made up. I didn't care if your foot was broken. It was not important. Pain had no significance."

I am listening intently to what I am saying, and suddenly it dawns on me that it doesn't make any sense. What I am saying just isn't rational. It lacks common sense to believe anything like that. I begin to talk to myself as if to a child: *You get hurt. You feel pain. It's the most obvious thing in the world. Pain is real. Body pain. Heart pain. Pain is real.* I let the words— *pain is real*—sink in. *Pain is real,* I assure myself again and again. I want this idea to soak into my muscles. Into my tissues. Into my brain cells. I imagine that I am the scary dark transforming myself into glowing light. I imagine myself accepting as true what my gut sense—*my intuition*—is telling me. That pain is real. It exists for everyone. *Pain carries an important message. And that message must be spoken and heard.* That is what I hear myself say.

Do you understand what an enormous insight this is, coming from a woman who always thought she was stupid?

125

Mary Patricia

I close my eyes and imagine freedom. It's as wide open as the ocean, and I am free-sailing across its blue waters. It's the freedom I have always longed for and griped about until I was blue in the face because I couldn't find it anywhere, no matter what I did. Now I *see* myself with wings. I *see* myself safe and cozy, gliding on gentle winds. I am on the brink of being free, finally, finally—really and truly free. *I know it.* I feel it in the deepest part of my soul. I can taste it. And it is better than any cigarette I ever smoked.

But there's more I have to do first—I know this, too. I *have* to unravel the dark mystery of *why* pain had no significance to me to. I can't go any further until I do. My freedom depends on this important understanding. I can't get out of it. To move forward, I have to answer this question—it is that serious. It is not as if the answer has not been with me forever, though. Sometimes I've felt it right on the tip of my tongue, but I refused to speak it. Most times I feel its pressure inside my body, squeezing me like a vice. But I constantly, *constantly* ignore it. Now once again, its shadow has climbed into my mouth, awaiting words, *my* words. The only words that count. Words that will lead me to understanding. Of this I am absolutely positively sure. I'm so thankful that I have another chance to get this right, after I've turned my back on myself a hundred times, a thousand times, a thousand times a hundred times.

Speak or die. That's my only choice. I can speak my way into freedom, solve the mystery of my hidden agony. Or I can withdraw and stay silent and allow the shadow—the pain—to eat me up again. Truth is, I'm too exhausted to live in the shadows anymore. The pain is too heavy to keep lugging all over the place. I don't have the gumption to keep running around in circles, hoping to find my freedom but only getting trapped in more quicksand. I have places to go now. Things I want to do. *Things I*

know I can do. So I *have* to finish this work.
I *have to finish this right now.*

126

Mary Patricia

The answer wets my lips. My words are a force pushing outward. I don't hold them back. In fact, I invite them. I applaud them. I simply open my mouth and out they pop, emerging loud and fully formed. Ripe red apples.

By denying pain, I protected myself from it.

I am shocked by the gall of my admission. By the firm confidence of my statement. Because I don't know where it came from. Yet I know it's true, I feel it vibrating inside me like an engine, shaking me from limb to limb.

What is happening? *What is happening?*

And then it occurs to me: my tender heart has completely opened itself up to my hardheaded brain and expressed the truth it has always known...and my brain is listening! *I am listening.* I am hearing.

Still, dead or not, I'm reeling something terrible from disbelief. One, because I'm actually listening to myself. And two, because this revelation connects. *It connects.* It connects all the pieces of me together. It connects the knowing in my heart to the sense in my brain. Somewhere deep, deep down inside, I must have always known this to be true — *I protect myself from pain by denying that pain exists.* I lived by the lie that pain is made up. My heart knew this was not true. My body knew this was not true. I can't live a lie anymore.

As if standing on a mountaintop, I state loud and clear, "By denying pain, I protected myself from it." I state this to the woman in the fog. I state this to the world. Loud and clear I state this to myself.

I think I might faint.

127

Mary Patricia

The woman in the fog massages my shoulders, keeping me calm. Reminding me that I am safe. I am valued. I am loved. I am strong. *I believe her.* Her belief in me encourages me to continue. "I wanted nothing to do with any kind of pain—*nothing.*" I sound like a robot spouting programmed, automatic words. Words not slept upon. Words reciting a rule pounded into stone. "I didn't want to see pain, hear pain, or think about pain. If I ignored pain, it wasn't there." The words ring as cold as the stone they are hacked into. The woman in the fog lays her soft hands on top of my head, and as true as I'm sitting here, sunlight immediately flashes through the kitchen and instantly I *know.* "That's how I lived," I say. *"That's how I survived."*

The second they spill out, those words ignite the weepy center of my heart and a gush of understanding sweeps through me. "Oh good grief... Oh good grief...*I was afraid*... Oh good grief, I was more than afraid...I was terrified. *Terrified.* Terrified that I would drown in pain. Terrified it would swallow me up and I'd die."

My friend's hands press into my shoulders. I think she's steadying me so I won't slide off the chair and onto the floor. I *have* to keep talking. I have to understand *more.* "I was afraid I'd *die.*" I sound so helpless, like a scared little girl frantic to run away. My throat is throbbing, aching to clamp shut. No, I won't allow that. Not now. Not after all this. I will stay calm. I will keep going. I am determined to understand this. I *will* myself to keep talking. I have to get to the bottom of the tank. "I was petrified that pain would kill me. That I'd die of pain, from feeling it. From feeling any kind of pain. Yours. Mine. Theirs. *But I still felt it.* Ornery Pat can testify to that. I tried everything to stop the pain. Ornery Pat tried everything to stop it. She tried to kill herself to stop it, for God's sake."

I reach my hands up to my friend's. I need to touch her, to be sure that she's still here with me. That she still loves me. She does. I can feel her encouragement. It lifts my spirits. I allow it. I sit silent and allow myself to feel my own courage. I feel its strength. I feel it swelling inside me. *You are capable, Mary Patricia. You are a courageous woman. A brave woman.* Whatever it is that I must face right now, I am capable.

I am a courageous woman. A brave woman.

128

Mary Patricia

Sister Bobby penetrates my thoughts like a dagger, carting her stink and filth. Once again I hear her threats: *You better keep your mouth shut.* I feel my innocent self buried alive, suffocating under her flab, squashed like a piece of rotten fruit. Frozen. Mute. Helpless. I feel her fists, blow after bruising blow. I am powerless in the face of her violence.

Once more I am drowning in the waters of the Delaware. Choking. Gagging. *Dying.* My screams ignored, forever silenced. A poetic melody meanders around in the currents of my memory:

...it is the river where I drowned. Where I died. They pull another girl out. Dry her off. Dress her in my clothes. The other girl. The other girl I do not know...

I whisper something strange into the heat of the kitchen: "From those days forward, I am a nobody, a shadow. A shadow sees no pain, feels no pain, speaks no pain. I do not dare. If I do, I will cease to exist."

The woman in the fog holds me. I am trembling and shivering against her. I think I might break into a million pieces. But I know I won't. I know I am capable. I know now that I can shake and shiver in fear and still move forward. I won't let fear hold me back from myself anymore. *Deep breath. Deep breath.* I am going to do it. I am going to do it. Another deep breath and I do it...I step across *the* threshold and wade into the place I have always been too petrified to go—into the seat of my buried pain.

The agony is enormous. It's not that I am feeling enormous pain; it is that I am *seeing* enormous pain. And there are no words to describe its size. It is massive. Its hugeness is beyond measure. It pulsates. And with each wheeze, it spreads its girth. It is a live, dark presence, the weight of iron. Uncarryable. Unmanageable. It is a growing, weighted force. *A planet.*

I see Pat. She is so small beneath it. It is crushing her, pressing on her neck, bending her spine. I watch the weight of the dark planet compressing her body, cramming all she is inside its hell, folding Pat in two. I see her bones wilting from its weight, unable to carry her any longer. I see her drained from the effort of dragging herself from place to place. I witness the spectacle of her buried pain rupturing inside her. I see the lethal poison it releases. I watch it contaminate her blood. I watch it implant disease. I see it gnawing and devouring without letup until Pat's insides are as twisted and contorted as her crippled outside.

Good grief, buried pain is a starving maniac feeding itself on whatever it can get a hold of. I see this as clearly as if I am watching a movie on the big screen. I am spared nothing as I witness the monster of my buried pain eating me alive.

129

Mary Patricia

Strangely, I'm not exhausted, though I think I should be. Fact is, I'm fascinated by this Technicolor vision of truth. What it is teaching me. It's as if I'm watching myself in a car crash and I'm mesmerized. I can't pull my eyes away from seeing myself airborne. Smashing through the windshield. Rolling along the highway. And landing in a crumbled heap in a ditch on the side of the road, dazed, until little by little I start to come to and begin to make out what took place.

That's what is going on right now. I'm beginning to realize the significance—the scope—and the realness of buried pain. It is registering with me—around here they call it *internalizing*—how pain feels inside and outside of my body. How pain feels like literal weight, pounds and pounds of extra solidified fat packed onto my frame. But I *have* to understand it, all of it. Uh-oh…I'm having a brainstorm.

I need to do what I never thought was necessary. I have to take the plunge. I have to wrap myself in all the horrible things that were done to me, all the things that hurt me so much. That's it. That's what's called for. I can *feel* it. It is like a calling. An urge I can't ignore. Well, I could ignore it, but it's not going to go away. It will just get bigger until it makes me sicker than a dog. And by that time, I'll have forgotten the whole point of why I was doing what I was doing, and then I'll be back at square one, sitting on my backside twiddling my thumbs and cursing, waiting around for some handsome prince to rescue me. That I know.

So, I'm going to do it. I'm going to immerse myself in the life that I lost, in all the beauty that was ripped from me, in all the wonder that was crushed. This is the only way I can think of that will help me *get it,* help me to understand, to remember that buried pain is *real* and it is a slave driver. It was my lord and master. My jailer. Buried pain was my punisher, and it trained me to punish myself. I have to remember this. My future depends on it. If I fall back into being lazy and wanting to lean on every Tom, Dick, and Harry, I will be doomed, all the work I've done squandered. And I will have to begin again until I learn backwards and forwards, inside and out, what I need to learn to satisfy the longings of my soul and walk the road of freedom I've been searching for my entire life.

I take a deep, deep breath and sink down, down into the dead weight of my buried pain, into its very center, and endure it for all it's worth. I don't shrink or look away. I pull upon something inside me that I did not know existed — I think this must be my courage — and ask myself to wallow in this pain. I touch it. I inspect it. I read it. Over and over again, I watch the replays of its cause. I study my face, my body language. I taste my closeted tears. I allow the feeling of terror to once again hammer my heart. I relive Ornery Pat's blistering rage. I face what was done to me and what was stolen from me until I think I've had enough, then I face it some more — frightening replay after frightening replay — because I thought none of it existed. Because I thought none of it mattered. Because I thought *I* didn't matter.

I study the living trauma of my buried pain until I recognize its disfigurement in my body, its roar in my silence, its scars in my brain. I inhale it. I review every single brutal second from every possible angle and record every single agonizing reaction until I know, *I know,* the truth. Because I have seen it. Witnessed it. Tasted it. Because I have lived it.

I know — *I see* — with certainty that I was brutalized. And that brutality can never be undone. I know — *I see* — with certainty that the consequences of personal violation are absolutely real. And I — my spirit, my soul, my body — paid the price in blood. I know — *I see* — now without a shadow of doubt where trauma landed me. How it sank my heart to the bottom of the tank. How it drowned me. Crippled me. How it left me helpless, frozen numb. Unable to move.

I see now that my children also paid the price for the brutal violations that killed my spirit. I know — *I see* — with certainty that they were hurt and violated...and blamed for the brutalities handed out to them. I loved my children with all my heart, but I couldn't protect them. I know — *I see* —

with certainty now how violence and cruelty contaminate the heart and spread like a plague. And become an out-of-control epidemic.

I know—*I see*—with certainty now that *I* am what is necessary to recognize the truth of my living trauma. By knowing and seeing is how I build my inner light—the foundation of who *I* am.

With loving compassion from the core of strength rising in my heart, I say to myself what I know to be true: *I am stable. I stand tall. I work from my light.*

130

Mary Patricia

I am very still, lying on a lush, grassy mountaintop looking up at a turquoise sky. My upper body where my heart rests feels expansive. Full to the brim as if my heart is swelling and deepening. It's a pure sensation. A meaningful sensation. I feel warm and safe. And curious. Because as I stare into space, I witness hundreds of snow white doves flying out of my chest and soaring into the brilliant heavens. If only you could see what I see. Birds rising with the wind and gliding in the breeze. Somersaulting in and out of cottonball clouds. Lone doves scribbling words across the sky. Flocks of doves flying in perfect unison, forming all sorts of letters.

I close my eyes and embrace the might and thunder of hundreds of messengers beating their wings in flight, pulsating inside my chest, throbbing inside my head—*breathe, Mary Patricia, breathe*—illuminating the gloomy inner recesses of my heart where I was jailed. Where every word important to me was imprisoned. Where tender love and great ideas drowned in the dark, freezing river of agony inside me, along with the drowned little girl. Where my voice died of strangulation before it could flower, its echo condemned to ricochet in a bitter cold, padlocked chamber.

It's taken an eternity it seems, but I am now committed to following my intuition. At long last *I* am listening to my story. I am listening to the truth inside me. That's how I am honoring myself, my spirit, my soul. I am learning to respect my experiences, not run away from them. My intuition was always the gateway. *Is* the gateway. The opening. The door. The entrance. The path. And the best part: I have given wings to my words. I can hardly believe it. Words—*my* words—finally released from their prison are, and always have been, the ticket to my freedom. I have set myself free.

I can fly.

Mary Patricia

I Love You

THE END

Mary Patricia

You probably want me to wrap this up in a neat package like a fairy tale. I can't. It wouldn't help you even if I could. Anyhow, that's not the way stuff works around here. Anyone who tells you different is trying to pull the wool over your eyes. If I could give you one piece of advice, I'd tell you, *Forget about heaven*—it's not what you've been led to believe. Life over here is much more than you can possibly picture—greater than you can even begin to imagine and harder than you ever realized. One thing: after you die, you take up right where you left off. Boy, was that a shock. I was convinced that death would fix all my problems. No such luck. Evidently, I read the wrong books and listened to the wrong people.

I didn't know that I could create my own happiness. I never knew either that all I needed to know was always right inside me; the only thing I had to do was trust myself. I never could get that part right. I wish I knew then what I know now. I could've told a very different story. If I'd been brave when I was alive, maybe I could've helped people out. Maybe I could've saved my kids a lot of pain. For me, it took dying to get down to business and learn what I needed to learn. Looking back, I see that every-thing I needed to find out about illumination and love was always right in front of my face. I just didn't see it. I didn't want to look. I was too afraid.

It's too late for regrets, but if I had my druthers, I'd sure do my earth life differently. I always had a choice, but I didn't understand that. I never imagined for one second that I had the courage anyway. Evidently, I always did have the courage; I just didn't know it. It's weird how courage works. I thought courage meant you always felt big and strong like you could take on the world. I didn't know that you could shake like a leaf and still do right by yourself and others.

Die and learn—that's how it was for me. I thought death was the road out of misery, that you would leave everything painful about your life behind and go on into Heaven with its perpetual peace and rest. Isn't that what they say to the dead, *rest in peace*? Or about the dead, *she's finally at peace now*? Don't bet on it, because that's sure not how it was for me.

But good grief, all my work over here is worth it—a thousand times, a million times over. I learned that the sooner you learn to love yourself, the mightier you become. And I don't mean being in love with yourself like a conceited snob, either. I mean really, really, honestly respecting yourself. Honoring yourself. Self-honor—that's how you get stronger and stronger. I'm so excited about being strong, feeling power inside myself. It's brand new to me. There's so much I want to do that I couldn't do when I was alive because hating myself got in my way. I'd say it crippled me something awful. I can't get over that I didn't see that. But I didn't. I do now.

Having a soul, that's the big thing. And listening to it has opened up a world I never knew about. But the soul's not an *it*...the soul is *me*. *I'm listening to myself.* Not to anybody else. How 'bout them apples? I'm learning about what I love to do. What I as a soul have always been con-nected to. I'm talking about words. *I love words.* And I always have. I'm on a real mission now to learn more. To see how I can work with words more and more. Doing what I love gives me so much energy—I'm glowing in the flow. I'm connected to love; love is connected to me. And my words are back! It all adds up to pure joy. And joy is the ticket!

"So," you ask, "who is the woman in the fog?" It's complicated. To me, she's my dearest friend. She's the meat, the center, the caring heart of my physical support, my emotional support, my spiritual support. She is the reflection of pure love. *She is pure love.* To you she is what *you* see. She is *exactly* what you need. That's the best I can answer, because you have your own answer to that question. Tell me...who is the woman in the fog?

Just to let you know, we did leave my house on Mark Twain Drive. Believe me, we left it spotless, too. We washed, dried, and put away every dish, knickknack and thingamabob we could get our hands on. The woman in the fog got the idea to scrub the kitchen floor on our hands and knees like I used to do when I lived there. I can't tell you how much I enjoyed dipping my hands in a bucket of Pine-Sol again, ringing out the old tee-shirt rag, and scrubbing that linoleum for all it was worth. When we got done, we could see our faces shining back at us. Now, that was heaven.

I won't be returning to Mark Twain Drive, there's no cause to. Going back there made me remember a lot of things about love I'd forgotten about. Love, that was the reason for returning there. That's what I surmise. Love is what pulled me back like a moth to a flame. Coming home to a place where I always felt warm and safe was fantastic. Feeling all those good feelings once again gave me the guts—*caused me* is another way to put it—to build a new life for myself. A life built on cooperation with myself. The best way I can put it is that Mark Twain Drive took up as solid ground for me and it was my job to build myself up from there. The way I see it is that I went back to a home I loved so much to build a home for myself inside myself. I turned my lights on, I guess you could say. And I allowed light to dissolve the darkness that fed my heart.

Earth terms aren't big enough to describe all that I've found in myself. All that I've discovered about living. And how much I'm looking forward to growing and expanding my knowledge and understanding. And using my words to increase other people's understanding of living and what is called death. Both are really about creating and radiating love.

There's joy in all that illumination, that's for darn sure. And I'm kicking up my heels and heading off into new horizons. See ya there!

Afterword

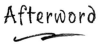

Kathleen

We need to talk.

We need to talk without hysteria. Without plunging into fear and denial and running away from what we do not want to be true. We need to talk about reality—about the pervasiveness of abuse, its destructive power, and the life-long trauma it leaves behind.

We need to talk about how the pain of unresolved trauma clings to our spirits, to our souls, even after we depart our physical bodies.

We need to talk about how sexual abuse is not over there—*it is right here*—right where we stand. We need to talk about how sexual predators hide *everywhere*. And we need to question why their victims are forced into silence.

We need to talk about how sexual abuse rages freely across all gender lines: girls, boys; boys, girls—the same as physical, emotional, and psychological abuse. We need to talk about how sexual abuse rages freely inside *all* age groups from the very young to the very old, and all ages in between—the same as physical, emotional, and psychological abuse.

We need to talk about how sexual predators lurk inside every group, organization, society, and culture, however defined—family; school; religion; social; volunteer; political; professional; and within all sexual and gender persuasions and orientations.

We need to talk about abusers and predators. We need to talk about the abuse of power—physical, emotional, psychological, spiritual, sexual. About social, religious, academic, and political systems that presume authority and issue commands that corrupt the right of free will.

We need to talk about structured systems that invent specific criterion that award power, privileges and prerogatives to a select few. We need to question why we give away our personal power to those few judged worthy by these systems. And talk about the impact and repercussions of this surrender.

We need to question why we tolerate and justify mistreatment of ourselves and others, including the vulnerable, and those rendered emotionally, psychologically and physically vulnerable by circumstances beyond their control.

We need to talk about victims of abuse. About how size, age, gender, appearance, education, social status, religion, and ethnicity offer no protection from violence.

We need to talk about the profound life damage inflicted upon victims by perpetrators and, thereby, society as a whole. And about how unresolved trauma impacts each and every one of us every day.

We need to talk about genius thwarted, creativity destroyed, potential abandoned. We need to talk about the sum total of what society sacrifices on the altar of silence and ignorance.

We need to talk about how giving voice to traumatic experiences is the pathway to understanding and recovery.

We need talk about celebration. About cheering trauma's excavation; applauding its exposure. We need to talk about transforming trauma's crippling pain into focused action and powerful personal authority.

We need to talk about supporting all visceral, artistic expressions of the dark forces of trauma. We need to talk about encouraging the use of *all words* necessary to communicate its truth.

We need to talk about what it means to be compassionate and sensitive, as individuals and as a society. We need to talk about setting and maintaining healthy boundaries.

We need to talk about horizons. And awareness. We need to talk about authentic freedom.

We need to talk more. We need to question everything. Then we need to do something.

Kathleen Hoy Foley
2018